To Blue Skies Liz & Chris

RIVER OF JANUARY ©
PART ONE

Best Wishes
Gail Chumbley
2016
Reno Air Races

by

Gail Chumbley

Point Rider Publishing ®

River of January Part One
By Gail Chumbley

Cover Design: Brooke Rousseau
Interior Design: Yvonne Rousseau

ISBN: 978-0-615-97683-9
ISBN: 978-0-9778964-2-4 (Get Around Publishing)
LCCN: 2014904047

Point Rider Publishing ®
www.point-rider-publishing.com

First Edition

Printed in United States of America

For David and Catherine, *my amazing children*

And to my husband, Chad,
who gave me his heart, and this story

A clouded moon
Creeps across the clouded sky
Winds of January sigh and moan
And yet it's June, I can see a sky of blue
Dear, the miracle is due to you, just you

"It's June in January"
Lyrics by Leo Robin
1934

Cristo Redentor
Artists: Paul Landowski, Heitor da Silva Costa, 1922
Rio de Janeiro, Brazil

RIVER OF JANUARY ©
PART ONE

Table of Contents

PROLOGUE

Helen Thompson

Montgomery Chumbley

Rio de Janeiro
(River of January)
Magic
1936

Wandering in from the casino, the three American pilots found their regular table near the dance floor. Paul sat with his towering back to the stage, and both Chum and Steve stared purposefully until he asked, "Is something wrong?"

"Look Bub, you're too damn big for this table," quipped Steve.

"Too big for this nightclub," chimed in Mont Chumbley, whose friends called him "Chum."

"Sorry fellas," the 6'5" friend wearily apologized, accustomed to the complaint. Paul, not bothering to stand, hopped his chair further toward the right and sighed. "There. Now I'm blocking someone else's view."

All three pilots grinned in comfortable friendship.

"Band's a little clangy tonight, sounds like they could use a couple quarts of oil," Steve critiqued.

"I couldn't say. I think my ear for music is a little plugged," Chum chuckled, a cigar in his teeth.

The house lights darkened, and the orchestra scraped out some opening bars. The three Americans shifted their attention toward the dark stage. Abruptly, a pink spotlight flashed brilliantly, revealing a breathtaking girl who caught Chum's interest. He absently wedged his cigar in the grooves of a crystal ashtray.

Her fitted costume may have been either blue or lavender; it was hard to tell from the tint of the spotlight—her swaying body seemed dreamlike, a hypnotic apparition, haloed in electric violet. The girl opened her mouth to sing, and at first he couldn't hear, but her strong voice rose above the uncertain notes of the accompaniment.

Her torso moved sinuously with a rhythm from her soul, the music how she wanted it, not the way the orchestra played. Her hair waved softly silver, her smile a warm window of goodness, the undulations of her perfect legs triggered his primal curiosity. The 27-year-old pilot stared, thoroughly hypnotized by the young beauty.

THE HEIR

The Farm
1927

Martha Chumbley had reached her limit. "No more delays—no more difficulties, no more deceit. You will sign Mont's enlistment papers," she insisted through tightly clenched teeth.

Mont's father and mother scowled at one another across the oval, pine table as if gamblers wagering for the highest stakes. The nervous boy watched from a stool against the rough wood wall, his eyes fearfully alive and fixed on his father.

Instantly, Jason Chumbley wheeled maliciously toward his son shouting, "This is your doing, you troublemaker!"

Martha wasn't about to let her husband undercut her case by blaming their son. She stepped between the two. "Stop where you stand, Jason. This is about you, now."

The hate in his father's eyes made it hard for Mont to remain seated. The old man never ceased to look for a reason to chastise his son—and this confrontation could very well end badly. He had never quite understood the hardness of his father's heart until an incident the previous fall when the father revealed his core resentment.

Jason and his lead man were inspecting the burgeoning, thick corn rows, deep in discussion about the upcoming harvest. Estimating the number of hired hands needed, their conversation soon turned to the many shortcomings of young Mont.

"Can we count on that boy of yours this time? He should know the harvest, sir. He's heir to this entire property."

Jason Chumbley shook his head frowning. "I blame that mother of his. She's raised him into nothing more than an insolent dreamer! She's treated him like he's better than the rest of us. Treated him like he's too good to get his hands dirty working the fields," he fumed. "I'm tellin' you, I don't believe I can whip that boy enough."

Invisible to the men, the boy had heard every threat his father had spewed. Hoeing weeds a few rows over, Mont froze in place, stunned by the venom in his father's voice, and in honest terror of being discovered and beaten.

He knew from past experience, that for any perceived offense, he'd be forced to pick out a stick from a wood pile. If the wood wasn't big enough, his beating became far more brutal. His father would order the boy to stretch bare-backed across the pile of stacked firewood, counting the number of welts, bruises and splinters as proof of a thorough whipping.

"I have watched you," Martha Chumbley shouted over the table, startling the young man back from his dread. "Whip and bully Mont, and try to grind him down year after year, all because he isn't like you. You drove him from his home, our son—exposing him to peril!"

The boy winced at his mother's impassioned words. He knew she didn't comprehend half the hell he had endured in the West Virginia coal mines, nor would he ever tell her.

*

An imported laborer from Poland tramped his way into the blackness of a deep, dank West Virginia tunnel. Only in the country briefly, the ragged foreigner, holding a lantern in one hand, had just exited the shaft cage. Balanced over his shoulder the worker hauled a short steel girder for use as structure support deeper in. Above the immigrant, suspended, stretched a raw electric wire, and that quivering line continued the entire length of the tunnel.

The boy watched as the upright girder just kissed the unprotected power line, knocking the hapless newcomer flat onto his backside. The boy had chuckled—painful as the jolt must have felt; Mont couldn't seem to stop himself. Then all humor vanished, as the Pole, attempting to regain some dignity, furiously roared to his feet. Brandishing the steel beam, the Pole deliberately attacked the line and instantly collapsed dead, electrocuted. As miners gathered around the smoking corpse, Mont realized there were worse places to live than Pulaski, and made up his mind to go back to Virginia.

"He is not a horse to be broken! His mother declared, jolting Mont from his revisited horror. "He doesn't find satisfaction in planting and harvesting and milking, and rising at four damned o'clock every morning."

Here, Martha took in a steadying breath and she spoke again, quietly, yet as forcefully. "There are more important things in this world than what you want, Jason. The world is a bigger place than this backwater farm," Martha Chumbley stopped, leveling her steely eyes at her husband. "You will go to the recruiting center with the boy and you will sign the papers that permit him to enlist. He's not asking you for anything else. He's willing to serve the Navy for however many years it takes to fly airplanes.

His mother, by now, was nearly spent with exertion and emotion. Harnessing her last shreds of strength, she stood up straight, addressing her husband with a voice that signaled finality. She raised her chin decidedly. "You should also know, Jason, that I've retained a lawyer in Pulaski who will advocate in court for Mont's right to enlist, if you fail him."

Jaws dropped. This commanding side of the generally mild Martha Chumbley had never before surfaced. The shock in the close little kitchen—from Jason and Mont— was revealed only by Jason's audible gasp. Both locked eyes onto the resolute farmwife. A clock ticked loudly from an adjacent room accenting the tension.

Gentle, kind Martha Surratt Chumbley carried a light touch. She had found her way to Pulaski some years before, seeking work as a milliner from Sylvatus, Virginia. Though the boy did not know the details, it had been there – in the shop – where soft-spoken Martha fashioned women's hats, that she met Jason Chumbley, was courted, and married soon after. The new husband then brought his bride to his ancestral home in Pulaski County. Three children later, and in the face of growing tension over her eldest son, Martha became a quiet shield for her offspring.

She had adapted to her rustic destiny with a sublime grace that defied her surroundings. After meals, she would rise from the table, flash her son a loving smile, then turn to shove another piece of pine into the black cast iron stove. Martha, with her practiced hands, popped a small hatch open, the handle as hot as the firebox. She inserted the wood, and quickly closed the firebox again without an oven mitt. He smiled at the fact that she made everything look so easy. Sadly Mont accepted that escaping his father's wrath meant leaving the warmth of his dearest supporter.

*

Mont's love of flight was an open secret on the farm. As a child he had watched, captivated, as a flying barnstormer landed a biplane on a wheat field near their farm. The pilot mesmerized young Mont with an afternoon of tricky loops, dives, and rolls. After that wondrous encounter, every time the boy heard the distant whir of an airplane, he would race outside and watch that miracle of engineering cross the sky. Martha understood her son's most ardent desire, and she would do anything to help Mont realize his dream.

In 1927, with the glow of Charles Lindbergh's flight across the Atlantic still burning bright, the boy had earlier prepared for the Naval Academy's entrance exam, which was administered down the road from Pulaski, in Washington County.

The exam was tougher than he dreamed, and Mont grew more and more disheartened with each wordy question. The arithmetic solved easily enough, but the language arts and reading sections became impossible. As he glanced at the other candidates, heads down working diligently, his heart sank. He quietly lay down his pencil and gave up.

By the time he reached home, the ambitious boy knew what he needed to do. He would enter the Navy by enlisting and would work his way to Annápolis through the prep school housed on base at Norfolk.

As Martha's ultimatum echoed in the silence of the small kitchen,

Jason Chumbley began to fidget. When other family members had learned that Mont considered enlisting, the news became quite a scandal on the farm. Many parroted America's own regrets, for the Great War had left a deep wound on the country's psyche. "It's beneath the dignity of a respectable family!" a brother carped. "The military is a refuge for scoundrels," added Jason's sister. Any Chumbley who joins military service dishonors our family name," Grandma Harriet grumbled over and over, until the idea became Jason's.

By the time Mont needed his father to come to the recruiting center, Jason had made up—and closed—his mind.

When Martha at length spoke again, her voice had softened, but not her determination. She leaned subtly toward her husband. "It's clear you don't really know, or understand, or care for Mont. He doesn't share your way of looking at the world. Why, then, force him to stay? You have plenty of other help. Let him find his own way, and at least try to seek his dream."

Within a month, on June 13, 1927, on his eighteenth birthday, Montgomery Chumbley formally entered the United States Navy.

THE NAVY

Norfolk, Virginia
1927

"Seaman Recruit Chumbley!" barked the petty officer facing the ranks.

"Aye, Sir," the boy snapped dutifully at roll call. Shifting his eyes, Mont caught the sailor next to him smirk hearing his name. When the men were dismissed, he challenged the wise-guy.

"You think my name is funny?"

"Well, yeah, I sure did. But now that you've turned and I see how big you are, I've decided your name is actually beautiful. In fact, I wish it was mine."

A couple of sailors hearing the exchange loitered close, hoping for some kind of dust up. When Mont laughed, the onlookers moved on, disappointed.

"In fact, you actually look like a Chum, the fellow recruit continued. "Name suits you. I think you and I could be chums."

From then on, the name Mont was used only by relatives and old friends in Pulaski. Among his fellow swabs, "Chum" permanently stuck. The rest of his basic training in Norfolk offered no real challenges for the healthy young man. He watched as some other enlistees, city boys mostly, found the training too rough. The Navy rejected a few recruits for adjustment problems—crying for their mothers or injuries on the training grounds. Chum was pleased to discover that his Petty Officer couldn't compete for mean when squared against his spiteful father. The young sailor actually relished the physical drills required by Navy regulations. He and the other recruits had to show firearms proficiency, reach daily physical training targets, pass personal and quarters inspections, and observe mandatory punctuality. Still, he felt unfulfilled. His dilemma—what kept Chum tossing after lights out—was calculating how to cross the abyss of rank that kept him from flight school.

*

Once through basic training, Seaman Apprentice Chumbley opened his first official orders, only to find the document made no mention of aviation. Instead he was ordered to crew duty aboard a coal-burning tug.

"My God! Have you ever seen such a greasy, black pestilence in your life!" blurted an exasperated deckhand toiling next to Chum on their first day of duty.

The tug, which escorted larger class vessels in and out of port, required regular maintenance. At the close of each workday, when the tug docked, the crew hauled out bucket after bucket of filthy coal cinders, which the sailors hoisted from the ship's cooling furnaces below deck. This endless volume of soot and ash settled fine oily dust over every inch of the ship, requiring daily scrubbing of the entire vessel.

"'Fraid I have," Chum muttered recalling his boyhood ordeal as a runaway coal miner.

Chum was surprised that this duty also triggered a relapse into horrific nightmares of the West Virginia tunnels, where he had witnessed hopeless suffering and needless death. The young man again fought for air, gagging on heaps of slag creeping into his ears and down his throat. His torture only ended when he woke in a sweat-soaked bunk.

His heart urgently hammering, Chum rubbed the sweat off his forehead, panting, *I might as well be buried in the shafts again. I can't get away from those damned black holes.*

Chum's pay for tug duty, with all the nighttime terrors it inspired, amounted to $26 a month.

*

"Name," mumbled a bored uniformed clerk.

"Chumbley, Montgomery J., Seaman Apprentice."

"The Naval Station offers radio, meteorology, navigation, and preparatory training for the Academy," he droned mechanically. "State your selection, sir."

"Prep training," Chum announced proudly. "I aim to enter Annapolis."

The clerk rolled his eyes and Chum realized he had probably heard that many times before.

"Instruction Room number 4D, tomorrow at 0800 hours."

Reporting on time for the first day's instruction, Chum found himself later in an assigned study hall battling to keep his eyes open. His busy morning had included remedial lessons on parts of speech and American literature, the boy's poorest marks. Now he sat at a desk, trying to review the morning's material.

A preposition is a function word...that is the most boring thing I've read today. He stretched and yawned. Tired of the tedious grammar text, he reached over to the literature book and flipped to poetry.

"Oh, Captain! My Captain!" he read. Staring at the page, the sailor wondered, *What in the world does 'Oh, Captain!' have to do with me flying airplanes? Except that I'd like to be a captain flying airplanes. Captain M. J. Chumbley. What about Commander Chumbley? Even better, if I were Admiral Chum...*

"I've notice how hard you work, Seaman!" the sailor suddenly heard from behind. "You appear to be a serious, ambitious young man."

The deep voice interrupted his daydream, causing him to bolt upright. Officers always made Chum nervous. "Thank you, sir. Just trying to get a little studying done, sir."

Chum recognized Lieutenant Edding, headmaster of the Naval Preparatory School, who in turn examined the young recruit closely.

"I've watched you, son, and you seem like a good egg," Edding paused, seeming to make a decision. "I was hoping you might consider helping me out of a bind."

"What can I do for you, sir?" he replied, honestly puzzled.

"You see, my wife and I have planned an evening out, and we can't find anyone to tend our children. I thought maybe, once you've put them to sleep, you could continue your studies at our home. We would pay you, of course."

Chum hesitated a moment, a bit stunned. At first flattered with Edding's high regard, he next turned a little pink with guilt. He really wasn't much of a student—expending more energy pretending to study than actually learning anything. However, the young man recognized when an opportunity appeared in his path. With Lieutenant Edding he might become acquainted with other ranking officers who could, perhaps help him reach his objective.

Chum smiled "I would be honored to watch your children, sir. You can count on me."

Not long after, for a second time, the young recruit challenged, and again failed, the Annapolis entrance examination.

BEATING THE ODDS

Hampton Roads, Virginia
1928

Word of young Chumbley's nanny services spread swiftly among the lower ranks. His buddies dished out a fair amount of ribbing, including his newest name, "Auntie Chum." But he took it with good grace. It wasn't long before the head of all base schools, Commander Charles Seymour, and his wife, also used Chum's childcare services.

The Seaman entertained the children with stories about the farm, the coalmines, or his horse back home. He'd send them to bed, and sit at the kitchen table, staring blankly at his books. Still, working for the commander offered some hope because Commander Seymour took a liking to him, and soon expressed a personal interest in the sailor's Navy career.

In fact, Commander Seymour read Chum's second set of failing test results before the young man knew his own scores. As before, Chum had failed the English section. Seymour, sympathetic to the young sailor, kindly offered his condolences. "Sorry about your exam, Chumbley. I think it's about time you become more realistic and consider other possibilities, son. You know we have a fine radio school here."

The boy answered the commander with a forlorn face. The kindly officer responded to Chum's devastated expression, patting him on the back. "Radio's the future in naval communications, trust me."

"I appreciate your help, sir, but please let me make a counteroffer. I'm not interested in radios," he spoke nervously, unable to stop himself, recognizing this was his moment.

"Listen young man. I will tell you the truth. Your odds of

surviving flight elimination are worse than the odds of your passing the academy entrance exam. No, son, no. Radio school's a safer bet."

"I'd really prefer flight school," the boy respectfully persisted.

"Radio school would release you from tug duty," Seymour persuaded. "You'd work in a more specialized and cleaner service."

Chum raised his eyebrows and produced his most charming grin. "But sir, I want to be a pilot."

The two batted the issue back and forth, until the commander wearily surrendered.

"Okay." He sighed. "I'll sign you over to flight elimination training at Hampton Roads, but only on one condition."

Chum's heart raced with hope. "What's that, sir?"

"When you wash out of flying—which you certainly will—you're on your way to radio school."

"Yes, sir!" Chum replied enthusiastically, guiltily aware that he had no intention of fiddling with radios.

*

Two weeks later, a nervous and sleep-deprived Mont Chumbley reported for flight elimination exercises. He joined 125 other candidates; smartly lined up on a long dock, facing the gray, choppy seas of Hampton Roads. From this windy spot would-be pilots underwent demanding instruction in ten-hour heats on various flight maneuvers. Day one: morning-takeoff, afternoon-landings. Day Two: mornings-turns, including the figure-eight, afternoon-climbing and descending turns—all in Curtiss NC4 seaplanes. Their instructors rated them at each step, either passing or failing, with no second chances. The pool of candidates became smaller with each roll call.

Feeling the pressure, the young sailor took special pains to follow flight protocol. Climbing around on wet pontoons fixed to the underside, Chum examined the biplane as it bobbed on the rolling water. He talked himself through each required procedure, so he wouldn't overlook any step.

"Oil leaks? Negative," Chum recited as he performed his pre-flight inspection. "Rudder locks off? Affirmative."

He continued crawling around the aircraft until he was sure his check was thorough. After the meticulous exterior inspection, he settled into the cockpit.

"Controls? Check. Stick?" He jockeyed the stick left to right then up to down, "Check." "Ailerons? He wagged the panels, "Check. Gauges?" He examined the calibrations closely. "Check."

Concluding the pre-flight list, the student-pilot ignited the motor as another crewman propped the biplane's propulsion blades quickly hopping back to the dock.

Chum, still repeating all he was taught, lifted the plane from the rollicking waves and then leveled the wings using the needle ball as he reached altitude. Momentarily surprised with the ease of his lift, Chum relaxed, in control of the little trainer.

This isn't that complicated, the astonished young man marveled. The thrum of the engine seemed calming, and he could practically feel the buoyant pontoons below the fuselage.

Flying makes sense, he reflected. *Pull the stick this way, up, reverse the stick that way, down.*

A sense of wonder filled the young man. As if born to fly he intuitively grasped the mechanics. *Flight requires gravity, logic, instinct, and sound equipment.*

The Curtiss biplane read Chum's mind, rising on a line, descending on an angle, turning on an invisible anchor point. The little aircraft did what he desired.

Of the 126 flight hopefuls, only nineteen succeeded—including Mont Chumbley. The washouts returned to Norfolk to ship out to sea, to labor on the hellacious coal burning tugboats or other maritime duties. Chum gratefully headed for warmer climates—flight training with his class, 37C, in Pensacola, Florida.

Thinking again of his mentor, Commander Seymour, Chum had to smile, *radio school would probably have been too difficult.*

HEART AND SOUL

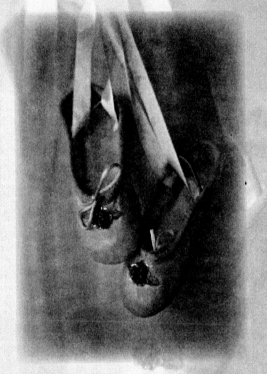

New York
1927

Helen, clad in a silver tutu, nimbly dashed off stage after the last encore. She slid on her toe shoes to a stop, bending at the waist to catch her breath. The young dancer had just finished her first genuine road show, Collegiate Revue, with this final performance at New York's Loew's Theater on Broadway. She, along with a small company of other young dancers had, with their final bows, completed a three-week tour throughout the Northeast, from Bangor, Maine, to Atlantic City, New Jersey.

At each stop the troupe entertained enthusiastic crowds of primarily young audiences. The seven-person company amused eager crowds with comedy skits, performing hit songs such as "My Blue Heaven," and spirited dance numbers. Helen energetically propelled herself onto the stage, kicking and stamping through the latest fads, including the Varsity Rag, and the new rage, the Lindy Hop. So with mixed emotions the girl, hugging an oversized bouquet of red roses, curtsied before her last curtain.

"Hello, my dear," she could hear from somewhere above and lifted her head, then her torso, to see a handsome couple facing her. The woman, dark-haired and thin, had a beautifully straight nose, dark dancing eyes, and a wide, kind smile. She spoke with a thick, European accent. Her male companion stood a few inches taller and sported coarse, curly hair. He wore a dark vest over a dazzling white, sharp-collared shirt.

"I'm Catherine Cansino, and this is my husband, Antonio." Helen took the hand Senora Cansino offered.

"So nice to meet you," she replied breathlessly.

"We adore your dancing style, Helen. May I call you Helen?"

Helen nodded. She was used to people coming up after the show to acknowledge their appreciation.

"You exhibit such a graceful combination of ballet and physical feats," the lovely woman complimented.

Helen grinned. She could hear the orchestra reprise the finale score, as cheery patrons shuffled up the aisles.

"We've never seen anything like it." The man finally spoke, and Helen listened as his words curled over each other.

"We dance flamenco ourselves." The smiling woman struck a classic Gitana pose, her right arm over her turned head, her left hand holding her skirt in the opposite direction and clutching imaginary castanets. Her spine was straight, and her heels close together, with her feet at opposite angles.

The man added, "We also perform fandango and cape dancing. We dance as a team, but we're always looking for other acts to add to our bill."

Helen felt they were waiting for her to say something.

"I would love to see your work," she said sincerely.

Catherine took Helen's hands in hers and searched the girl's eyes. "You could my dear. Would you like to join our dancing tour? We start here in New York and then travel south through Maryland, eventually ending in Texas. Do you know when this production will end?"

Though only sixteen, Helen was intrigued, ready for more adventure. She percolated with excitement—this elegant couple was offering another, extended road show, and they wanted her. Texas!

Helen tried to appear serene, older, and professional. "We are closing Revue now." She nodded toward the stage. "But I'd have to talk about all this with my mother. She's my manager."

"Of course. It's nice your mother supports your career. We're staying at the Iroquois, just off Times Square. Why don't you, or your mother, call us and we'll discuss contract terms. How does that sound?"

"Fine—good—grand!" the dancer sputtered, her dignity forgotten. The couple chuckled as they glided toward the stage door.

"Thank you!" Helen called after them. The lady waved back with her white-gloved hand.

*

Helen's mother, Bertha, paced in front of the apartment window, from one end of the living room to the other, on slipper-clad feet.

"So young, she's so young. And for such a distant and lengthy tour... Are the Cansinos truly respectable people?" she muttered anxiously.

Helen watched her mother, only interrupting when Bertha paused for a breath.

"I've been performing professionally for two years, Mother. I can do it. The Revue wasn't much different, and that went by just peachy. Mr. and Mrs. Cansino are obviously decent people, Mother, and I know about caution—especially on the road."

Bertha glanced at her stunning, younger daughter sitting on the sofa. "Helen, Wilkes-Barre, Pennsylvania is in no sense the same as San Antonio, Texas. I never expected that a dancing career could take you so far from home. What would your father think? Would he have allowed it?"

"Papa lived on the road, Mother. If anyone understood traveling shows, he did," Helen countered.

Bertha, still obsessing, didn't acknowledge her daughter's point.

"But we do need the money, Lord knows," she finally yielded.

Bertha had met the Cansinos for dinner the previous evening, and Helen knew her mother had no misgivings about the couple. Both seemed like conscientious performers, professionals who could accomplish a lot for her daughter. In fact, while enjoying coffee after the meal, Bertha had brightly suggested that she could chaperone. The Cansinos tactfully turned her down.

"Our accommodations are too limited," they told her, "We have arranged rooms for the two girls together. You see, we have one young girl traveling with us already."

Helen had to smile at her mother's ceaseless effort to stay close.

Three days later, mother and daughter taxied to Grand Central Station together. There, Helen kissed her pouting mother goodbye, hopped up from the platform, and waved at Bertha until she disappeared from view.

She found a seat with the Cansinos next to the window in their berth and watched the passing landscape unfold. The train sped by small towns where children waited on whitewashed fences, pumping their fists—a signal for the engineer to toot his whistle. Further along she noted small brick churches with white steeples, dense forests of birch and pine, and farm houses surrounded by checkerboard fields. Helen passed her hours chatting with her new employers and imagining the lives of the people who lived in those little dwellings along the line.

> *Dear Mother,*
>
> *Our train reached Baltimore and we played a theater called the Ehmling's Music Hall. It is rather old, but so are some of the acts that play there. Yuk, Yuk. I've met a nice girl I room with. Her name is Leonie and we have loads of fun traveling together and playing shows. Leonie's favorite pastime is taking pictures of the cast with her camera. She often catches us sleeping with our mouths open or hamming it up for her. I am being very good and staying safe, so don't worry. I miss you and will write again soon.*
>
> *Love, Helen*

"This is oodles of fun, isn't it?" Helen asked Leonie on a morning train headed to New Orleans.

"It is for me, but don't you miss your mother?"

"Actually," Helen admitted, "I do and I don't. Life on the road is so exciting, so educational! Until I met you, I had no idea dish soap removes stage makeup."

Leonie giggled as she said, "I still can't believe no one told you that."

"My mother is swell," Helen reflected, "but needs me close to her. I don't notice so much when I'm in New York. But to tell you the truth, when I'm away I enjoy making my own choices."

She paused, her forehead creasing in thought. Then she stretched her arms and legs. "I feel like the world is brimming over with possibility!" she exulted.

The tour changed its name in Louisiana from "The Cansinos versus Jazz" to "The Cansinos in Flamenco Versus Jazz." This new format featured modern dance pitted against traditional American and Spanish forms. The playbill listed high-energy pieces with lively competitions between "old" and "new" in popular music and dance.

Helen contrasted both styles skillfully, alternating traditional ballet with raucous popular jazz. Beginning with a delicate Swan Lake, she would suddenly revert to the Black Bottom, stamping each foot and then both feet, arms undulating outward, while she shimmied around in a box-step.

Then there was the popular Charleston, where she would swing her right arm and left leg, then alternate her steps in a bouncy expression of joy. Seamlessly, the dancer would return to graceful ballet, ending her solo with a series of ten ballet spotters, spinning grandly. Both steps were delivered with such sparkling energy that the audience frequently gave the girl a standing ovation.

One afternoon rain was falling when Helen and Leonie stepped out of the stage door after a rehearsal. They had arrived in New Orleans the afternoon before, and had performed the previous night. Hurrying back to their hotel ahead of the rest of the company, they decided to take their umbrellas and tour the streets near the wrought iron balconies of the French Quarter.

"It sure is coming down!" Helen exclaimed. "Glad my mother talked me into taking an umbrella!"

"I always take mine along when on the road," Leonie agreed.

"How many tours have you been on, Leonie? You're not much older than I am."

"Well, let me think. I started in vaudeville with my father. Mother traveled with us back then. After they both died of the flu, I moved to my grandmother's." Leonie sighed.

"And?" Helen prompted.

"And, nothing. My grandmother never welcomed me, and I left after winning my first audition. That's all," she said as she shrugged.

Gazing at her companion with new eyes and new admiration, Helen sympathetically took her hand as they walked, their black umbrellas bumping off beads of rain.

"Helen, look!" Leonie whispered. She pointed a finger to a weathered wooden sign over a shabby storefront shop. "It's a fortune-teller. Let's see how much it costs."

"You don't believe in that hocus pocus do you, Lee?" Helen asked.

"I don't know if I do or if I don't. But I am curious. What if she, or he, can tell us if we will be stars? That's worth a little money, isn't it?"

The dancer thought about it and then caught Leonie's enthusiasm. They stepped through the milky glass door into a bleak, bare room. Little bells shivered on the door as it shut, and from behind a red satin curtain a woman dramatically emerged. She was beautiful, with shiny black skin and jeweled black eyes. She wore a long electric blue robe with a white turban coiled around her hair and long silver earrings dangling from both sides of her exquisite face. Despite her beauty, something in her expression terrified the girls.

"You want to know what awaits you in the future," the woman stated.

The two held hands and stared, frightened by the fortune-teller's certainty.

"I am known as Mara, and I see things," she explained, as though the girls had asked. "You," she pointed to Leonie, "You want to know if you will always be alone."

"Yes?" Leonie croaked.

"And you," she proclaimed, focusing on Helen. You desire to find success in your life. Mara can answer your questions."

Stunned to have the woman state their business, the girls were asked for 25 cents each. They thought the charge was high, but were too frightened to either leave or protest. Mara gestured for the two girls to follow her through the scarlet drapery. They squeezed their hands tighter together as they complied.

"She said I would leave show business!" Leonie complained after the woman had talked to them and sent them off. "It's the only work I know. What would I do married to a farmer, raising children and chickens? I'm a city girl!"

Helen laughed.

"And you, Helen!" Leonie continued. "How did Mara phrase it?" Leonie rasped in a mystic voice, "A man will rule your heart," she murmured, "While another will command your soul."

"You could find a career as a mimic, Leonie." Helen grinned. "But that isn't what I paid to hear. She didn't say a thing about being a star."

Leonie frowned. "Did you have to giggle when she was predicting your future?"

"Honestly, Lee, my heart and my soul? Nobody really says things like that," Helen scoffed.

"At least whoever it is won't be a farmer with chickens," Leonie shook her head disgusted. "And, we paid her money for two lousy predictions."

The next month, in September, while playing the Majestic Theater in San Antonio, Helen Thompson celebrated her seventeenth birthday. It was 1929.

*

The three women trudged home in the dark, as early snow silently fell on 45th St. Mother Bertha, with her older daughter Eileen, and Helen, newly returned, had enjoyed dinner out, followed by a moving picture at the Capitol Theater.

"Al Jolson has such an expressive voice." Bertha's words puffed into the cold air. "His singing doesn't have quite the richness on the radio as it did in that movie."

"He's a swell actor, too," Eileen chimed in, her breath vaporizing in the dark, cold, New York night. "I loved the scene where he explained his passion for singing popular music to his mother…and she understood."

Helen trudged alongside in the deepening snow saying nothing. Her thoughts were drifting three thousand miles west in Los Angeles.

"Didn't you like *The Jazz Singer*, Helen?"

"Oh, Mother, yes, yes, I did. It was astonishing. The sound resonated from every direction at once. I felt like I was part of the film."

That evening at the picture show made a profound impression on the dancer, her mind turning over the wide-ranging prospects for sound in film. Nights later Helen, still preoccupied, stretched out on the worn carpet at her mother's feet, thumbing through Variety magazine. Bertha concentrated under the same lamplight, in a tattered wingback chair, mending a torn pocket on her old housecoat. Eileen lounged on an old, floral sofa under a pedestal floor lamp, reading Agatha Christie's *The Murder of Roger Ackroyd*.

Helen suddenly asked, "What do you hear from Aunt Ednah?"

"Hmm, who…? Ouch!" In her surprise, Bertha pricked herself with a needle. She set her mending in her lap and stuck the injured finger in her mouth.

"Whoops! Sorry, Bert," Helen shrugged. "Aunt Ednah" she repeated. "I've been thinking about her, Uncle Harry, and those droves of tiny Afghan puppies roaming everywhere on the lawn."

"Well, dear, I haven't heard much lately. What made you think of them?" Bertha probed.

"Mother … Bert?" the girl sat up as she addressed her mother. "What would you think about visiting Hollywood?"

Surprise colored Bertha's face, while Eileen curiously looked up from her reading.

"Listen to me, Mother. Vaudeville is struggling we've seen how hard it is to get good parts. I've hardly worked since the Cansinos' show."

Bertha opened her mouth, ready to argue.

"I know, I know. A couple of theaters. Now listen to me," Helen cut her off. "The future of show business is the movies."

Bertha tilted her head, considering her daughter's point.

"Movies have sound now, marvelous sound," Helen's voice grew animated. "This means musicals can be filmed in Hollywood, and audiences can watch dancing and singing without buying a ticket for a Broadway theater. Film directors will need dancers who can sing—dancers who can deliver lines. Dancers like us," she beamed, looking at her sister.

Bertha looked thoughtful.

"Would you like to give Los Angeles a try?" Bertha asked, looking at Eileen.

"I can't let you go without me," Eileen responded. "Who'd I pick on without the little squirt around?"

Helen hopped up, hugging her mother as she shouted with joy, "Nifty!"

*

Bertha, Helen, and Eileen left Grand Central Station in September 1930, headed for Chicago, where they would transfer at Union Station to the train called Union City of Los Angeles.

This journey lacked the lighthearted sense of adventure Helen experienced on her solo tour with the Cansinos—although the family did enjoy eating in the dining car and squeezing together into their sleeping berth each night. The cramped space launched all three into fits of giggles. Through the car window the Thompson women watched the passing lush fields, the tall yellow grasses of the central plains, and the barren brown southern plains shifting into the burnt southwest.

Soon, gently rising into the southern Sierras, they traded the yellow-brown of the desert for the gentle green of temperate California. After a four-day journey, they embraced a pleased Aunt Ednah at Los Angles' Union Station.

BEATING THE ODDS

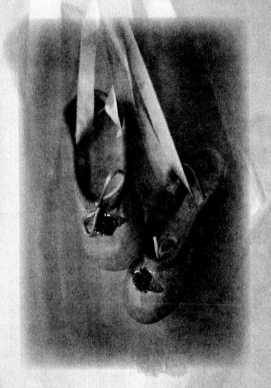

Los Angeles
1930

"Because he is married," Bertha coldly articulated each word, as she admonished her daughter.

Helen's eyes popped as she glanced at her married dance partner, Grant. "How do you know? How'd you find out?"

"No, Helen. That isn't the question. You knew and you didn't tell me!" Bertha squeezed the back of a chair slat so tightly her knuckles whitened.

Helen kept her voice even. "I didn't tell you because you'd react this way, Mother. There's nothing... "

"Stop!" Bertha's eyes pierced through her daughter, "You have talked enough!"

"Honest! Nothing is going on between us," Helen bravely continued, standing in her aunt's living room. She peered first at Grant, who glared icily at her mother, with his arms folded tightly and his fists flexing, and then at her mother who appeared nearly unhinged.

"And now you want to travel on tour with this married man? Just you and this man alone? Helen, what has happened to you out here? I raised you with better morals and standards!"

Weeks earlier, when Helen and Grant Garrett, an aspiring comedy writer, had first met they had struck up an immediate friendship. Grant had placed an ad in the trade papers for a partner, preferably someone who knew ballet. Tall, slim, and magnetic, with dark eyes and curly dark hair, Grant appeared to be a flirtatious Casanova. But with Helen, Grant acted more like a kid— playful and funny.

"I grew up in Los Angeles.," he had told Helen. "I've written comedy scenarios for silent film directors, such as Mack Sennett."

Helen gawked like a tourist. "You know Mack Sennett?"

"Yep. I've also written music and gags for vaudeville acts such as Olsen and Johnson, and I've written radio bits for entertainers on both coasts."

"Wow!" Helen was impressed.

"So you're in luck—I'm fooling most of the people most of the time," Grant chuckled at his own cleverness.

"Have you performed your own material, Grant?"

"Oh. Yeah. Sure." Grant sipped his coffee. "I've played around town with other partners, on the radio, and in dinner theaters."

Helen nodded again. "So, why do you need a partner?"

Grant set down his cup, moving his hands in the air while talking. "Well, see, I've written some gags that require a ballerina of sorts. You're very pretty, Helen. Are you sure you know ballet?"

The girl stood up on the dimly lit stage with a sly grin. She rose up on her toes and immediately spun a perfect series of spotters.

"Okay. Don't get carried away, kid, you probably have the job!"

"Probably?"

"Well, don't hit Bloomingdales quite yet. I've got a couple other auditions. But you're at the top of my list." Grant leaned back, stretching his long legs, the legs of a dancer. He prodded, "Tell me more about yourself."

Helen described her training and experience, telling him she grew up in New York, lived with her mother, sister and for now, her aunt. She explained she found it a challenge landing work during the economic collapse.

"We—my sister and I—were both given this letter when we registered at Central Casting. It was so depressing, Mr. Garrett. Things look as bad here as they do in New York."

"It's Grant," he corrected, taking the document she handed him from her purse.

He scanned the form letter, honing in on a series of numbers,

For the 17,541 actors registered with Central Casting on Hollywood Boulevard, plus the several thousand not

under contract but vying for parts, only 840 jobs exist. Unregistered extras largely play non-speaking parts in large crowd scenes. Of the 10,000 women registered this year, only 21 of them worked more than 3 days a week. But if you offer a specialty—a foreign language, training in a musical instrument, or singing and dancing—you improve your odds of employment.

Grant whistled, looked at the dancer, and remarked, "You just might beat those odds, kid."

*

Helen had conscientiously sought work before her audition with Grant Garrett. As Eileen trailed further and further behind in her bookings, the younger sister pounded the boards and took whatever jobs she could find.

The dancer paid calls everywhere—nightclubs, radio stations, theaters—orbiting ever outward through the greater Los Angeles area. Carefully, the girl listed her many stops in a small address book—the Westlake Theater on Sixth and Alvarado, the casting office of Fox Western Westwood Studio, and Paramount Studio—leaving her latest glossies and a contact number.

In between calls, she continued training at a dance studio near her aunt's home. Hearing of any openings for extras, especially for a musical, Helen marched through numerous theater doors, dragging her reluctant, older sister behind her, as they both auditioned for parts in countless chorus lines. The sisters stuck together for most open calls, yet they rarely landed parts in the same productions.

"This number requires dancers to appear in sequined briefs and halters," announced one casting director to a crowd of hopefuls. "If you have any objections to body exposure, we cannot use you."

As veterans of vaudeville, neither girl flinched—partial nudity was just another part of show business. If the job paid, the girls would perform in nearly any costume

Helen studied the movie industry with a business-savvy eye, noticing that, at first, motion pictures seemed resilient to the stock market crash. The global market continued to clamor for American-made films.

By the time the Thompson women arrived in California in 1930, Helen counted five major studios that dominated the scene as Hollywood powerhouses: Warner Brothers, Famous Players (Paramount), Joe Kennedy's RKO (Radio Keith Orpheum), Metro Goldwyn Mayer, and 20th Century Fox.

Smaller companies, which seemed to hire more often, included Universal, United Artists—co-founded by one of Helen's favorites, Charlie Chaplin—and Columbia Pictures.

All were busily churning out an avalanche of small budget films.

From her time of performing on eastern stages, Helen knew the large studios owned theater chains across the country. Contract actors were counted as mere studio assets, reduced to chattel by signing long-term agreements, rendering the movie business a more glamorous version of the factory system. Studio chiefs, such as Jack Warner or Louis B. Mayer were only more glittering robber barons forced to share their company town.

The bleak economic depression that shrouded the country moved the studios to produce lighter fare. The screens were filled with formulaic musicals and comedies, ornamented with extravagant sets, dance lines, and stunning stars in stylish costumes. Directors like Busby Berkeley and the anarchic and brilliant Marx Brothers produced song, dance, and jokes, aiming to dispel the hopelessness shadowing everyday life in the America of 1930.

Helen, undaunted by financial barriers, or statistics on form letters, doubled her efforts. And the girl's perseverance paid off. She landed the role of "giggling girl in the harem" in 20th Century Fox's "Women of All Nations," directed by Raoul Walsh.

"Look, Mother," Helen proudly held up a notice. "This is my official gate pass into Fox Studios."

"You will, of course, usher your mother through that gate for a visit. Correct?"

Helen teased back, "Hmmm ... maybe ... if you're good. To tell you the gospel truth, B," Helen affectionately addressed her mother, "the movie is rather silly. But I did meet the stars, Victor McLaglen and Bela Lugosi."

"You did?"

"It's not like you think, though, Mother. We actually stand around a lot, rehearse, and then finally shoot a scene. The big stars come out and just sit around with us, as we all wait. It's much like a company of troupers in a stage production."

Bertha's expression fell a little, as if she had just learned there was no Santa Claus.

"I've met some nice people though, Mother. There's this nice boy, Humphrey Bogart, and a funny comedian named El Brendel."

Eileen quietly pushed open the bedroom door where the three slept, cuddling an Afghan puppy in her arms.

"How's the movie, squirt? Is it going to be any good?"

"I think that one is really sweet," Helen remarked watching the dog.

"Don't let it wet on the floor. Aunt Ed will flip her wig. The story in this movie follows two Marines, Flagg and Quirt, as they chase an exotic girl around the world. She's played by Greta Nissen."

Bertha sat down. She'd read that name many times in movie magazines.

"In my scene," Helen continued, "I slap a Marine who I think has pinched my bottom, but everyone in the audience is in on the joke. The culprit is a hidden monkey riding in the pocket of another Marine."

"My, oh, my," Bertha sighed, deeply impressed.

In another successful audition, the girl landed a part in United Artists' "Scarface," appearing with star, Paul Muni. This time she had a small walk-on, entering stage right with two other extras, and then bowing a couple of times before exiting. Helen returned each night to entertain her family members with new stories of celebrity encounters.

*

"What I want," Grant Garrett explained to Helen, "is a sidekick for my jokes." He gestured as he spoke. "I'll be standing on stage running my hopefully amusing dialogue, while you slowly, keeping a straight face, execute one ballet pose after another, as if I don't exist. Do you think you can do that?"

She smiled. "I don't know. Do you want to try it?"

A tall thin janitor, toting a mop and bucket in each hand, shuffled up the aisle and asked, "You folks finished yet?"

Grant glanced at the man, and then at Helen. "No, not quite. But you can help us. How about you sit down and watch?"

The curious janitor planted himself in the front row, watching as Grant took Helen's hand and led her to the center of the stage. The few other maintenance workers watched as Helen extended onto her toes and gently curved her arms over her head in a graceful pose. She ignored Grant and everyone else, standing as silently as a statue.

Grant started his routine, shifting slightly from one angle to another, but always facing his audience. "I was single for a long time, and then got married. Got tired of finishing my own sentences."

The small crowd chuckled, then watched as Helen, on her toes, swung her arms down close to her sides, bent over slightly, and undulated her arms as if they were wings. She fluttered her fingers, moving her still vertical toes up and down like pistons. She turned slightly away from Grant.

The comedian ignored Helen, too, addressing the nearly empty seats, "I went ice fishing last week. Fried it up and nearly drowned!"

The audience laughed, and Helen crouched, placing her empty hands flat on the stage. Slowly, defying logic and gravity, she extended her legs into the air.

With now rapt onlookers, Grant felt he should do more. "The eternal question' of why the chicken crossed the road has finally been answered." Grant nodded his head toward Helen. "She's poultry in motion."

As Helen slid to the floor into the splits, her legs straight out from her hips, she couldn't stop herself—Helen broke up laughing, straddled flat on the stage.

When he pulled Helen up, they stood together, still snickering. Grant brightly addressed the head janitor, "I got a couple of bucks burning a hole in my pocket! Step out, squire, and bring us some champagne."

The worker, chuckled, shook his head then resumed his mopping; Helen remarked, "Your idea seems to have worked. They're all grinning."

"They are, aren't they? The old noggin can still hatch a sketch or two, can't it? Well, what do you say we get our own champagne, kid?"

*

Grant had been initially charmed by Helen's pretty face. But, before long, he began to admire more than her appearance. The entertainer respected her work ethic and her imaginative suggestions. The partners spent hours a day in rehearsals, pounding on the piano, and dropping accidental bloopers, playful pratfalls, and riotous improvisations. Helen's dry comedic timing synchronized well with Grant's witty, verbose give-and-take, and they frequently spent more time laughing over the lines than finishing them.

"Rill Wogers, Helen? Try Will Rogers, kid, and let's start again." She folded to the floor in an exhausted spree of laughter. Grant plunked down next to her, amused and captivated.

Eileen, often out of work, sat in on her little sister's rehearsals. After one particular session, as the two girls walked home down busy Hollywood Boulevard, the curious older sister asked, "Is something going on between you two? Between you and Grant?"

"Something, Eileen?"

"You must see the way he looks at you."

Helen stopped walking.

Eileen noted her sister's stunned face. "Oh, Helen, you have to see that Grant's in love!" They started walking again. "How do you feel about him?"

Helen hesitated. "I don't actually know. I've been so busy with rehearsals and thinking of my career, I never thought about that kind of relationship. He's older than I am and I'm sure he's married. Sometimes he calls me Babs, and I figured that's his wife's name. But when it comes to his professional judgment, well, Grant knows what he is doing.

Eileen burst out laughing. She poked Helen's arm. "Goodness, Mother and that crabby old dance teacher, Mr. Evans have certainly trained you well."

Helen stepped back, hurt.

"I don't mean anything by that." Eileen nudged Helen lightly. "Just that you're quite the single-minded career girl."

"Don't misunderstand, Eileen. I believe in true love. There's someone out there who'll carry me off to happily-ever-after. And I do have feelings for Grant. He's my boss and the source of the wonderful material and choreography we perform. But we can't concentrate on personal things. We have to work on the act, and make some money!"

"And he's married," her older sister quietly repeated.

*

For a chance to perform and generate income, Grant proposed the tour that Bertha so vehemently opposed. He had added new dance numbers to showcase Helen's versatility, and worked up fresh skits and gags. Grant would toss out a seemingly bland line and Helen would retort while standing on her hands or stretched into a full backbend or even posed in a formal arabesque. Grant's favorite gag was timing his dialog so he directly answered Helen's feet, as the girl perched in a full handstand when he spoke.

"Our material is strong, Nell," Grant exclaimed to Helen, using his pet name for her. But, babe, those casting calls have dropped off steeply. This just in ..." Grant mimicked radio announcer Walter

Winchell. "The Depression has officially hit Hollywood. Details at the top of the hour."

"It's fine for the big studios and their stars," Helen shook her head. "The Lew Ayers, the Gary Coopers, and the Jean Harlows—they all rule the motion picture industry. But, those of us breaking in need to work further and further out of the city—Orange County, Long Beach, as far from Hollywood as we can afford to drive."

"Don't worry, Helen, I will make Garrett and Thompson a success. You can trust me," Grant put his arm around her shoulder with an encouraging squeeze.

*

As Bertha ranted over Grant's marriage, he stood his ground, fuming in Ednah's living room. When her mother paused for a breath, Grant gritted his teeth and spoke slowly. Sounding calm he said, "It's true. I am married. But I'm separated from my wife. We have no children. And when my divorce, or actually our annulment, comes through, I will no longer be married."

Bertha quietly retorted, "I'm not sure that would make me feel any better about your interest or intentions with my daughter."

"Well, you see, then, she and I might as well go on tour and make some money... which will give you time to figure out my motives," Grant stated. "For now, making a living ought to do."

"You can trust us, Mother," Helen soothed. "We won't do anything disgraceful. And the act is top-notch! I'm sure it will be a hit."

"Helen." Bertha chided, "So naïve."

"I will look after her," Grant flatly assured.

The mother glared.

Helen broke in, "You said yourself last week that Aunt Ednah can't keep us forever. I can help with that, Mother. Won't you please give me your approval?"

Helen's words hit their mark. Bertha, too, knew the film industry as well as Helen. She realized very little work—in radio, film, or theater—existed. After a tense silence Bertha spoke. "I will allow you to go on tour with him under two conditions."

Helen held her hands in front of her mouth. She stood on excited tiptoes without realizing it.

As Bertha laid out her first condition, she glowered at Grant. "You keep your hands off each other!"

Helen nodded in agreement while Grant remained glacial.

"And my second condition is this," Bertha continued, "You must return to us in New York when the tour ends."

"What? New York? Are you leaving?"

"Yes. Eileen and I will return home while you're on tour. Your sister feels anxious to return to our apartment in New York. She prefers familiar theaters and contacts."

Bertha strode to Grant and looked at him, coldly, straight into his eyes. "I will order Helen home straight away at any sign of impropriety on your part. That's a promise."

Grant held up both his palms. "There won't be any of that, Mrs. Thompson. I can assure you."

However, the mother felt no reassurance. Agitated, Bertha abruptly left her puzzled daughter and Grant, stomping outside, joining her aunt seated on the lawn. "I can't lose her, Ednah. I have already lost more than I can bear," tears rimmed Bertha's eyes. Aunt Ednah tenderly reached over cradling her niece's hand.

*

Twelve year old Bertha Locke leaned over the top drawer of her dresser, while her mother neatly folded a stack of clean laundry, placing clothes carefully into a black steamer trunk.

"Why don't you and my Father live together?" the girl blurted suddenly. Her mother, paying no attention to the outburst, continued to pack.

"I think you should take the red wool scarf for winter, don't you agree?" her mother responded. "It's mighty cold at that school in Michigan." She held it up for Bertha to consider.

The bedroom they worked in, though not large, was well lit and brightly furnished. Mother and daughter had been visiting Los Angeles, at the home of Minnie's cousin and best friend, Ednah Marxmiller. They had been in California since June, and now were preparing for their fall pilgrimage back to Ohio, followed by Bertha's delivery to school in Gross Pointe. Their comfortable surroundings were evidence of Aunt Ednah's and Uncle Harry's growing affluence.

Undaunted, Bertha gazed up at her mother, again demanding, "And why don't we live in a house of our own?"

Minnie dropped some stockings in the trunk, sighing as she sat on the bed. Still avoiding the question, Minnie asked, "Don't you like staying with Aunt Ednah? I thought you loved her."

Bertha glanced down, her bottom lip set in a pout. "She's strict, but I do love her. And I love her huge house. And the canyons, the ocean, the beaches, and Catalina Island!" Her eyes lit up as she proclaimed emotionally, "I love Los Angeles!"

"Well, then." Minnie squeezed her daughter's hand in finality, and returned her attention to the trunk.

All Bertha knew was that a conflict between her physician father, Frank Locke, and her mother, had split the couple apart. Perhaps he was untrue to her. Or her to him—but she couldn't imagine that scenario. The little girl could not bear the thought of her mother betraying anyone, but sometimes around men…

No! It had to have been her father. Perhaps he missed dinner too often, house calls keeping him from his family. Maybe her physician grandfather kept him at the hospital late into the night, tending patients. Nonetheless, the girl could not recall living with him. Nor could young Bertha fathom why her free-spirited mother needed to pull up stakes and constantly move on.

She had no siblings. Since the girl could remember, it had been just the two of them—mother and daughter, wandering from home to home, residing with relatives. She had been only a toddler when Minnie packed their things, and they never again lived in Bertha's birthplace, Newport, Kentucky, on the south bank of the broad

Ohio River.

Her mother, Minnie Bates, a local debutant, grew up across the river from Newport, in Cincinnati. The Bates family rarely crossed over the bridge to visit the strange world of Newport, or anywhere else in Campbell County, Kentucky. That area had an unsavory reputation for rampant vice, which pushed respectable people to make their homes in outlying localities. It had been from the north bank, in Cincinnati, where shy and reserved Doctor Frank Locke met, courted and soon married Miss Minnie Bates. Years following their mysterious divorce, Bertha had rarely visited her father in Newport, and he gradually faded into a secondary figure in her life.

After a season, returning to Los Angeles, mother and daughter were welcomed back to Aunt Ednah's for summer break in 1901. Prancing into the grand house after a day at the beach, Bertha challenged herself to leap the stairs two at a time, bounding up to her mother's bedroom. Minnie had been ill a few days, and Bertha hoped to deliver some cheer. However, the eager fourteen-year-old raced unexpectedly into a wall of people hovering over, and blocking the bed.

"Why are you all in my mother's room?" she suspiciously demanded.

The somber faces of her aunt, uncle, cousins and a man she didn't know, caused her own heart to drop. She fought her way to the side of the bed, and then gasped at what she saw, her knees threatening to crumple. Minnie's face was pallid and lifeless, still on the pillow, and her hands folded on top of each other, resting upon her silent chest. The little girl collapsed.

Later, when Bertha revived, she found herself in her own bed, her aunt in a chair at her side. Bertha hoarsely whispered, "My mother, Auntie?"

"We don't know." Ednah, red-eyed, shook her head sadly. "The doctor thinks it might have been Bright's disease. Her kidney's failed, but for such a thing to happen to a woman in the prime of health, at her young age..." Ednah again began weeping.

A sudden boom against the wall made both aunt and niece jump.

Clumsily four men, strangers to the girl, side stepped down the hall, past her open door, carrying a long wooden crate. The man who had leaned over her mother's bed, a doctor, perhaps, followed.

Horrified, Bertha screamed, "NO!" Ednah instantly reacted, reaching the girl in time to grasp her arms securely, and pull her back down on the bed. Using all of her strength, the aunt held on to the girl as she shrieked and thrashed, flailing her arms and legs, trying to reach her mother's casket.

Bertha desperately wailed, until her body failed to support her grief. Each time she pictured her mother—Minnie's still, waxy corpse—tears would spill again, with a fury. The young girl couldn't escape her torture, or her bed. Nor could her throat guide down a morsel of food. The young thing was utterly hollow, lying on her back, staring vacantly at the ceiling through empty, pointless hours.

Days passed, and Ednah feared the girl would follow her mother if she didn't begin to revive. Bertha turned away anything from the kitchen, becoming so weakened that her cousins each took shifts to sit with her. They re-braided her disheveled hair the best they could, helped the girl on to her chamber-pot, and sponged her off from a wash basin. It was four days of silent nothingness, until she wordlessly tottered from her bed, struggled into the first dress she touched, and sat blankly through her mother's funeral service.

Weeks after the burial, fragile Bertha received an unexpected letter from her father in Kentucky. Aunt Ednah, uncharacteristically tender, carefully read his note aloud to her ghostly niece. And, as she read, she scrutinized Bertha's face watching for any sign that the young girl might relapse into catatonic despair.

> *Daughter,*
> *I was deeply pained to hear of the death of your mother. I know you will miss her, and hope you do not make yourself sick with your grief. Please know that I have missed you since the day you and your mother left this house. Your visits have seemed all too seldom.*
> *My dear, dear Bertie, I would like you to come live with me*

here. I have a comfortable situation, and can offer you your
own room. You have many cousins and younger siblings who
would love to know you. We can become papa and daughter
again, and I will do whatever possible to make you happy.
                                    Your loving father

Aunt Ednah spoke quietly, "Bertha, dear, I know this is all very hard for you. But, your Uncle Harry and I think it best that you go to your father, and try a change of scenery. Here, you are constantly reminded of the tragedy. In Kentucky, you can start all over again. In time, everything will seem better. You'll see." Ednah patted Bertha's limp hand.

Bertha dully absorbed what her aunt said, but she knew there was no solace to be found, anywhere, to relieve her sorrow.

She didn't know how to take the next step, her mind utterly unable to grapple with any more upheaval. Bertha dreaded living among strangers in Kentucky, where her father had remarried and started a new family. And she hated leaving California, though she understood her relatives believed she belonged with her father, and wanted the best for her. She certainly did not want to stay if she were a burden to her aunt and uncle, who had already done quite a lot for her and her mother.

The traumatized girl, numb with grief, unable to advocate for herself, dutifully boarded a train and traveled to Newport. Once there, her father and stepmother treated her with kindness, always asking "How are you feeling, dear?" But, Bertha felt nothing. Her world had imploded—vanished. She found herself lost amid a sea of strangers, some she was compelled to call brother, sister, father and mother. Instead of overcoming her devastation and healing, the girl grew more silent and withdrawn each day she spent in this alien world.

Her father wasn't deceived. The doctor in Frank could see Bertha deteriorating before his eyes. And so, on a snowy December evening, he sat his daughter down in his study. Though the room was jolly, with bright holiday decorations up to the high ceiling, she appeared tiny, nearly embryonic in an oversized stuffed chair.

"You're not happy here," he began.

Bertha drooped further in the chair, the toes of her shoes turning in. She said nothing.

Frank sighed and held up his empty hands in surrender. "We don't know what to do for you, and I cannot bear to see you so unhappy. Can you tell me what you need?"

"I want to go home," she said flatly, as she lifted her head and held her father's gaze. "To Los Angeles."

"That wouldn't be too painful for you?"

"No more than staying here."

"I was hoping that living with me would..." his voice trailing off. "I thought maybe...would you stay until Christmas?"

Bertha dropped her eyes to the floor, saying nothing.

Her father sighed with resignation. "Well, it's off to the train with you then."

By the end of the week, the girl was packed and on a train heading for southern California.

Arriving at her aunt's, Bertha quietly unpacked her things in her familiar sunny bedroom. Busily reclaiming her little space, she happened upon a letter sitting on the bureau, addressed to her. Her Aunt must have placed it there while she was still traveling. It was postmarked from a Cincinnati law office. Puzzled by the return address, she slit open the envelope and read,

> *Dear Bertha Georgie Locke,*
>
> *Our legal firm wishes to extend our sympathies on the recent loss of your mother. In her last will and testament, she named you as her sole beneficiary. This behest will provide you with a modest allowance to cover your living expenses until you reach the age of twenty-one years (21 years). At that time, the balance of the estate will come under your control.*
>
>

Sincerely,

Martin Alward

Alward & Price
>

As the forlorn child stared at the words, her wounds ripped open and fresh tears spilled anew. Yet, despite her pitiless suffering, she also comprehended that her mother's financial gift would allow her to continue to live where she felt the least miserable—a place with a niche in the family. She could pay for her room and board— pay her own way. Dimly, through her sorrow, Bertha was strangely reassured. "I'm not a destitute cousin needing shelter and charity. I can live where *I want.*"

SMART WESTERN STEPPERS

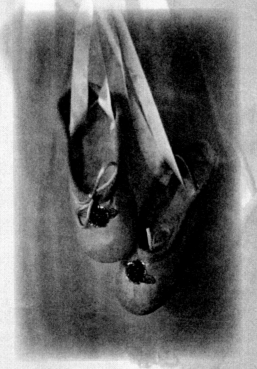

Traveling Cross Country
1931

The traveling comedy team of Garrett and Thompson left Los Angeles in August, 1931, on a train bound for Fresno, where Grant had booked an engagement at the Wilson Theater. From there, they continued north to San Jose, San Francisco, Portland, and Vancouver in Canada. There the two played at The Strand Theater.

The couple reentered Washington State, performed in Spokane's Fox Theater, and worked steadily from September through February, appearing in 24 more venues as they headed east.

All of Helen's earnings, as well as some of Grant's, made their way east as well. It went to Bertha in New York, as Grant labored to avoid any telegram, letter, or even worse, a personal appearance ordering Helen home.

The duo tirelessly put in multiple shows a night, with the final curtain often falling near midnight. Afterward they would join other acts for post-show parties, which typically howled until dawn. They often woke late in hotel rooms of varying quality and cleanliness—tawdry dives to grand suites. After rising, the team sipped their coffee, chatted softly, and lingered over a late breakfast.

By early afternoon Grant and Helen stepped again on the stage and rehearsed a couple of numbers, performing at six. Then their break-neck schedule began again.

After a booking closed, the pair would mend and clean their costumes, pack, rush for the train station, and speed to their next stop.

Each theater held its own surprises. Sometimes it was a clumsy, sour band in the pit.

Grant would roll his eyes at Helen, and she would answer

with a shrug in amused resignation. Sometimes they were delighted by a skilled, rich orchestra. Grant would wink and Helen would signal back with·her own wink. Then both partners hopped on the downbeat, and with radiant smiles broke into an exuberant soft shoe. Sometimes, the audience was lifeless or hostile and the jokes fell flat. On other nights roaring laughter thundered through the hall.

"These dumb natives," Grant once observed of a crowd along the way, "They don't know we need new material, and they holler at everything!"

On another night he wryly noted, "The damn orchestra pit's more populated than the audience. But we got more laughs in three days than the act gets in three years."

As they danced and sang their way across the country, Grant constantly honed their skits, which now included "Horse and Cornet," with its droll dialogue and impressive dance techniques.

"Horse and Cornet" went like this: Grant directed his lines to the audience as he ignored Helen, while the girl appeared bored. She leisurely switched from one ballet pose to another, delivering her lines with a blank face and a monotone voice.

Grant: I saw a horse wearing a coronet.

Helen: You mean playing a cornet?

Grant: No, wearing one.

Helen: That's ridiculous. How can a horse wear a horn on its head?

Grant: That's it; it's on a horn on its head!

(Helen turned a blank look to the audience)

Grant: The coronet covered the horn.

Helen: A cornet is a horn.

Grant: Not when you're a uni-cornet!

The comedian shot an impish glance toward Helen as he began to improvise. "Black Beauty... now there was a dark horse." He snapped his right fingers, then patted his fist. "Out at the stable all the horse-man-knew-er." Grant's ad-libbed joke caught the girl off guard. She swallowed a giggle.

When Garrett and Thompson eventually reached New York, a friend of Grant's called him long-distance from Los Angeles.

"Hey, Garrett, I just heard a morsel from your skit, Lady Love, at a dive in Hollywood."

"What?"

"Yeah. Seems your act is so slick it squirted back to Los Angeles."

"The creeps are stealing my material? Just wait till I get back."

"It means you're good, Bub."

"No, it means someone's gonna need stitches! I'll pummel anyone I catch doing it. Those bits were written for Helen."

*

Grant had booked performances along a meandering route from Denver to the Audubon Theater in New York. Arriving late in Denver during a blinding Colorado snowstorm, Grant and Helen found their billing was cancelled by a manager who couldn't pay them.

Evening gloom set in as Helen unpacked her trunk. Pocketing her room key she hurried down the corridor to join her partner for dinner. But Grant had disappeared. Growing alarmed, she searched the hotel most of that evening. She didn't find him until morning— asleep on an upholstered sofa in the hotel lobby. Grant, soaking wet, sported one blackened eye, a split lip—his left cheek swollen purple and blue. In his right fist, the skin on his knuckles raw, he clutched a roll of cash.

Helen gently shook his shoulder. "Grant," she whispered. Then, louder, "Grant, are you all right?"

He slowly opened his one good eye. "Hello, gorgeous."

Despite her sleepless night, Helen smiled at his swagger. "What happened to you? I was so worried."

Grant tried to sit up, grunted in pain, and slumped back against the cushions panting.

"Sorry kid. Bad rib, bare-knuckle matches. Outskirts of town. Fight rings, every night. Excellent return on my investment," he gasped trying to smile. With each word he moaned, his lip cracked further, oozing fresh blood. "Take this." He weakly held out his smeared fist to his partner.

Helen gently pried the bills from Grant's fingers and slid the money into her sweater pocket. "Let's get you cleaned up and in bed."

Grant nodded, grimacing as he again tried to sit up. Helen tugged gently on his arms. She got him off of the couch and they staggered together to the lift.

*

Grant faced a worse situation in Kansas City. The team was deep in rehearsal blocking out dance steps to a new number on the stage. Grant expressively read from a rewritten script, "Saw my old friend Charley yesterday, and he had a black eye."

"And how did your old friend get a black eye?" Helen replied, easing into a backbend.

"Well, he asked his wife where she wanted to go for their 10th wedding anniversary and she said 'Somewhere I haven't been in a long time.'"

Helen raised her right leg nearly to her ear as she asked, "And where did he suggest?"

"The kitchen!" Grant responded as a passing stagehand snickered. He hurried into his next joke.

"If April Showers bring May flowers, what do May flowers bring?"

"I'm stumped. Mr. Garrett; what do May flowers bring?"
"Pilgrims," Grant hit the punch line.

Then Grant set up the next joke. "Miss Thompson, I have kleptomania."

Turning into a pirouette Helen stopped, replying, "And what precisely is that?"

"My doctor says it's an illness."

Helen inquired, "Is there medicine for it?"

Grant finished, "Believe me, I've taken nearly everything!"

Their piano player, the only other person in the large, paneled auditorium chuckled, while he warmed up on the keys.

And then, from the dark tiers of the empty audience, they heard, "Hello, Helen, dear."

Three pairs of eyes peered into the gloom, and there stood Helen's mother in the center aisle, crisp and proper in coat, hat, and gloves, her suitcase at her side.

"Mother!" Helen released Grant's fingers and dashed down the few stairs and up the aisle crushing Bertha in her arms. "It's so good to see you!"

Helen leaned back, and mother and daughter looked each other over.

"You look better than I expected," Bertha remarked.

Helen grinned. "I'm very well. Come, Mother, say hello to Grant." She turned back to see her partner disappearing off stage left. "Grant!" she called, but he was gone.

Bertha, incensed, refused to tolerate such impertinence. "Follow him!" she screeched at the accompanist. He simply looked at the outraged woman and began fingering the old favorite, "A Hot Time in the Old Town Tonight."

*

Though Garrett and Thompson began their tour reading mixed reviews in local newspapers, their act became more polished with every curtain call. In South Bend, a reporter described the pair as "smart western steppers" and commented, "Miss Thompson was especially appealing and talented," which pleased both partners.

Grant joked, "You're the smart one. I'm just a western stepper!" In a more serious voice he continued, "Your ballet, Helen, that amazing ability to bend and turn while delivering lines really raises the audience out of their chairs."

Helen blushed and said a quiet "thank you" at Grant's unexpected compliment.

By November 1931, *Variety* described their Chicago performance as "solid." "Personality, here," *Variety* went on, "counted more than experience and ability...the girl had a lot of it, irresistibly accented by a knitted outfit that tickled the eye, and helped make her end of the gag delivery sound much niftier than it otherwise would...customers agreed they were promising."

Journeying northeast from Illinois, the show traveled to the Kent Theater in Portland, Maine. There, Bertha again materialized. While Helen hurried to change in the dressing room, Bertha tracked down Grant before he could make his escape. She again reminded him, "Just so you know, I'm never far away, and that girl will never be yours. She will be a star, leaving you where she found you, at the bottom—a cheap vaudeville nobody."

Grant stared daggers in reply. No longer did he feel reluctant to express his dislike. The dancer seethed whenever Helen mentioned her mother's name, or when the shrew suddenly appeared. This love affair was costing Grant plenty, his money, his body, and his heart. To enjoy unbroken time with the girl he now knew he loved, he was forced to mail Bertha the bulk of both their earnings—$195 for a little over two months of work—to hopefully keep the woman in New York.

He knew the mother would not hesitate to order her daughter home, crushing his hopes, and destroying his future happiness. And Grant's frustration at having no money to show for their hard work fed his considerable temper.

By Springfield, Massachusetts the team's money shortage grew serious. Kneeling on her hotel bed, Helen shook her purse until the lining hung out, searching for coins. Grant ransacked his jacket and pants pockets, even running his fingers through the elastic pockets of his suitcase. Angry, Grant spewed, "Twenty two cents, Helen. We have, between both of us, twenty two cents!"

Grant, as he often did, resorted to tracking down a bare-knuckle fight to raise quickly needed cash, and to enjoy the pleasure of beating someone senseless. He subjected his body to frequent battering to remain with the girl. And his time with Helen, all the same, was running out as their run of engagements neared the end.

Not willing to give Helen up without a fight, the suitor had one more card to play. After their final performance at the Audubon Theater, back in New York, Helen announced to Bertha, "Grant's setting up a new tour across the South."

"You won't go." Bertha said, with finality.

Helen, by now was as enamored with Grant as he was with her. Astonished by the intensity of her feelings, Helen realized her day couldn't start until he appeared for breakfast. She adored how his animated expressions sparkled as he described some new joke or routine he had dreamed up. And there was no one Helen trusted more than Grant Garrett. He had kept his vow made to her mother, as well, keeping his desires tightly wrapped. Many nights it wasn't Grant, but Helen, who had to be cooled off, and pushed out the door.

Facing her mother in New York, Helen kept her voice steady. "If I don't go, Mother, I cannot support you."

"How dare you use that tone with me! You've been gadding about the country with a married man! If the relatives knew, I would be mortified. I *am* mortified." Bertha slapped her palm against the tabletop. "And, is he nearer divorce than before? No!"

Bertha drew in a deep breath. "I let you participate in the first tour for the publicity—and the income, yes," she grudgingly admitted. "But, this is enough! You will look for work here in New York with your sister."

So, once again, Helen and her sister answered scarce audition calls for a few weeks—and found very little. Bertha reluctantly relented and again permitted the girl to join Grant on a new tour. He had stayed quietly at the Algonquin Hotel, taking calls, making calls, writing, and waiting out his nemesis, Mrs. Thompson.

Smug and not surprised at the turn of events, Grant and Helen again began rehearsals, finding time together more thrilling and gratifying than either had anticipated. The tour of theaters through the Deep South began in Washington DC, then stopped in Atlanta, and then moved the next three weeks west all the way to Phoenix, where the tour—and their partnership—ended at Phoenix's Fox Theater.

Partially secluded behind a soda machine at the Phoenix train station, Helen held a ticket east to New York while Grant waited for his train back to Los Angeles. He leaned against the wall as Helen pressed tearfully onto his chest. Eyes cast downward, alternating tears with laughter, the couple clutched one another desperately.

"All out of ideas," Grant whispered.

"And out of time." Tears freely fell down Helen's cheeks.

"We won't be apart long, I swear," Grant whispered, stray tears tracing his cheeks, too.

"Promise?" Helen quietly demanded.

"When we next come together, it will be forever. You will be my wife."

The two had shared nine bonding months—generating skits, performing in the best and worst of conditions, before gracious and spiteful audiences, rehearsing, joking, laughing, comforting, and treating each other's wounds, whether physical or emotional.

Despondent, the girl later curled up next to the window of her railcar, fighting back tears, and racking her brains for a way back to Grant. I guess I should be dreading mother's wrath when I get home, she considered. "But even Bertha's screaming and ultimatums won't keep me from Grant. Somehow we have to find a solution to this separation. I can't see any life without him."

FADE TO A
WHISPER

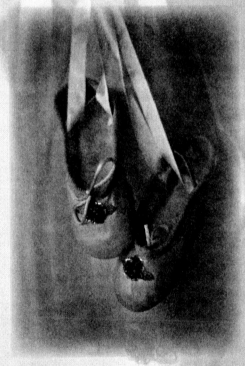

New York
1931

As Helen unpacked in the room she would once again share with her sister, Bertha sat on the edge of the bed, her hands twisting in anger. "You will *not* see that man again! He is no good for you. I won't allow it!"

Helen opened her mouth to speak, but Bertha snapped, "I won't hear another word about it— this subject is closed."

She brusquely stood and marched to the door, suddenly turning around. "You may contact him once more, informing him of my decision."

Before Helen could utter a plea, Bertha flew out, slamming the bedroom door behind her.

Following her mother's orders, Helen wrote to Grant one last time:

> *My Dearest,*
> *There is no way to deliver this message nicely. Grant, Bertha has forbidden me to contact you or see you again. It's not what I want and doesn't change my heart in any way. I need to figure out a solution so we stay together. I already have some ideas I am working on to get around her. Remember that I love you, and we will be together soon—on the stage and after the curtain falls.*
> *Your Nell*

Grant wrote back furiously:

> *That manipulating, old nightmare! How dare she dictate your*

life! You're an adult, Helen. Stand up for yourself—stand up for us! I have lived on my own for longer than I care to think, and I actually like my parents; I even eat there once in a while. But, Helen, they don't run my life—my father asks how business is going, then shakes his head doubtfully. Mother wants to know if I'm eating. That's all. Don't you support that woman? Aren't you your mother's breadwinner? Aren't you old enough to live your own life?

Now, enough with the sermon, and it's not you who causes me to see red. So please don't fret Little Nell. I will accept the challenge and fight for you. Rescue you, even if—especially if—you can't do it for yourself.

Love, Grant

*

After Helen's memorable trek across the country, the Thompson apartment in New York felt especially suffocating and lonely. Worse, the city's theaters were swamped with job seekers and few parts were available. She halfheartedly accepted work, venturing out of the city again with her old friends, Antonio and Catherine Cansino. Helen's only consolation came from the letters she received regularly and secretly from Los Angeles.

A solution presented itself during a sudden afternoon cloud burst in Manhattan. "I need a big favor, Dot," the lonely dancer divulged to her childhood friend..

"Sure, Helen," Dorothy Schiff answered cheerily, as the girls waited out the rain beneath a café awning. "It's fun helping you, especially if we're putting one over on your mother. Do you remember the night we told your mom we were sleeping at my house, and went into the city?" Dot smiled slyly as she crushed out her cigarette under her black pump.

Helen forced a half smile. "It was worth it. The ballet was magnificent. But, I would still die if mother found that one out. You see Dotty, I miss my sweetheart badly and he misses me. But

Bertha has put the kibosh on my contacting him again. Would you be a pal and let us use your address to exchange letters?" Helen, feeling guilty asked, looking down.

"You bet!" Dot crowed with pleasure. Helen was startled at her friend's enthusiasm.

Though deeply devoted to Grant, Helen still could not openly defy her intractable mother. Why Bertha loathed Helen's young man—he was getting a divorce, after all—remained a mystery. She regularly cursed Eileen's early slip up, tipping off Bertha about Grant's marriage. Just maybe they could keep this new correspondence plan with Dot under wraps.

Eileen, realizing how much Grant meant to her sister, vowed to make no mistakes this time. And it wasn't long before Dotty happily began to rotate Grant's letters to Helen and Helen's letters to Grant— thoroughly enjoying the intrigue.

Dearest Nell,

So everyone remembers you from our last time in Philadelphia. I don't doubt that a bit. You leave quite an impression, kid. But I'll bet everyone on Broad Street remembers old Bertha and her high jinx the night she showed up! I need to tell you, darling, with you gone I had to audition a new girl for my act. But don't worry. Her boyfriend dogs her closer than your mother hounds you! It doesn't matter though. Whenever I write new bits, I envision you performing them.

There's a lot of jobs out here, dearest. I know a producer and a director looking for someone just like you. If you come back, you won't lack for work. By the way, does Bertha suspect you of receiving these? I'm amazed she hasn't demanded that you stop thinking of me. With you there and me here I feel so lonesome and homesick ... lonesome for you and homesick for what? You again, and again, and again...

My darling Grant,

Please hold on. Everything will turn out all right. She'll come around. *Mother doesn't realize how great you are, how talented. After your divorce, she won't have any reason to object. Be patient, love, and finish that divorce.*

Love, Helen

Sweetheart,

Wait, you say. Wait. Miles do make a difference. You think your mother will change her mind about me? On the level, Helen, how will you explain where you've been, what you've been doing, during the time you're reading my letter? She'll ask—and you have her becoming my best friend! I sometimes wonder if given an ultimatum, would you choose me or her?

G.

Dearest Grant,

Please don't be annoyed. It's easier right now for me to go along with Mother and to find work here in New York. I wouldn't have a career or have met you without her help. She needs my support right now. I see your face when I close my eyes, hear your voice as I fall asleep. Know that every ounce of me loves you from long ago until forever.

Oodles of Kisses,
Helen

Sweet Baby O' Mine,

Received your hot letter today and take back anything I said about you cooling off. Edges only scorched. I've been boxing, in the ring this time, to regain my former svelte figure—all for you—but now I fight with gloves to protect my delicate hands. Helen, come back to me. Until then I'll stay true.

Gee

Dearest Girl,
  Does our affair gradually fade to a whisper?   A day's
silence, a day away from you, leaves me in the dumps.
                                                  Gee

Letters of love weren't enough—Helen longed to be with Grant. She lay awake at night pining for a way to have Grant in her life and keep her mother happy. And she deeply yearned to return to Los Angeles and into his open arms. Yet, more powerful was her fear of, and deference to, her mother's wishes. And that fact overruled any challenge the girl was willing to raise about Grant.

At that time an opportunity, a new job, presented itself, rescuing Helen from her dilemma—an opportunity made more appealing by the participation of a renowned dancer that the girl was keen to meet.

It started when walking home from a clandestine postal visit to Dorothy's, Helen stopped by a newsstand, picking up a copy of *The New York Times*. She carefully hid Grant's newest letter in the business section, where her mother wouldn't see it. Her step was light and confident as she tripped up the stairs to the third floor.

"Bought a paper, Mother," she announced as she closed the door. "You want any of it?"

Bertha stepped from the miniscule kitchen, drying her hands on a red embroidered dishtowel, "Pull out the entertainment section— I'd like to look at the motion picture schedule. I have a hankering to see that new Gable movie, *No Man of Her Own.*"

Clumsily pulling folded paper out of the layers, Helen casually dropped Grant's letter into her jacket pocket, turning toward the bathroom—the only private room in the apartment. But she had no time to reread his vows of love and heartache.

"Helen, what are you up to?" Bertha called from the living room.

"Just a minute," the girl called from behind the door. She shoved the letter back in her jacket and flushed the toilet for cover. Quietly, she padded into her bedroom, lifted her top mattress, and concealed Grant's note inside with the rest of his correspondence.

In less than a heartbeat, Helen returned to her mother.

In an animated voice, Bertha read, "Promoters behind the new ballet tour have enlisted the celebrated ballet mistress, Maria Gambarelli, for a new European excursion."

"Gamby? Europe? Are these open auditions? Is there a telephone number?" She and the rest of New York radio audiences knew Miss Gambarelli very well.

Maria Gambarelli, an Italian-born, American-raised soloist had studied under the legendary Russian dancer, Anna Pavlova, and rose to appear in motion picture cameos, and headline at New York's Capitol Theater. The renown ballerina then moved on to radio, billed as one of "Roxy's Friends" featured on Sam "Roxy" Rothafel's broadcast, where she earned the pet name of Gamby, charming listeners with soft-spoken Italian tales and folk tunes.

By 1927, Miss Gambarelli presided over the new Roxy Theater as prima ballerina. Her dance company adopted the name the "Roxyettes," in honor of the beautiful new venue. As a part of her tireless campaign to educate the public on the splendor of ballet, Bertha continued to read, "Gambarelli has agreed to host auditions for this new tour at the Roxy, and to organize a new travelling company she has named *The American Beauties*."

Bertha, bubbling with excitement, gently took her youngest daughter's face into her hands, "You must audition. This could be our big break."

Later, drifting back to her room and lost in her imaginings, Helen laid down on her bed. Europe and Gambarelli—the prospects of such a tour swirled her daydreams in spirals.

"Grant's letter!" Helen gasped, remembering his note under her mattress. Rolling off her bed, the girl grasped for his envelope.

> *My Darling Girl,*
> *Strangest thing happened driving to Long Beach for a show. You weren't with me. I still can't get used to turning around and not finding you in the backseat. It ain't right, Nell. I have been faithful, haven't chiseled at all, not once! Wouldn't cheat*

on you even if Greta Garbo was naked in the bedroom.

Ah, Helen, I've been all at sea here waiting on you. And you, waiting on her. Are you cooling off? Your letters sound that way. Please write me the dirt, honey. Are we any closer together than a month ago? I once told you if we ever got separated we'd never be together again. And I still believe it. Still waiting on Babs to file. Should hear any time. Well, I guess I'm going to have to rehearse another new girl, if you don't come west, but Helen I am still—always—true to you.

G.G.

Helen's eyes blurred over Grant's neat, boxy printing. She slowly folded his letter and slid it again between the mattresses. Slumping back on her bed, the girl buried her face and cried. She realized that the possibility of reuniting with Grant had been an illusion. She mournfully decided not to respond to his note. And the love that had been so urgent, so joyous, and so passionate quieted into a sweet memory, and through the passage of time, into a fond friendship.

*

Early for Helen's Gambarelli audition at the Roxy, the girl and her mother crowded among throngs of other hopefuls. Mothers pulled distracted daughters through the bedlam, while their girls dawdled behind in rounds of hugs and squeals of excitement. All the dancers were dressed in rehearsal skirts, tights, and leotards— toe shoes slung over shoulders, or around necks. A pianist, oblivious to the chaos, loudly played echoing chords from the stage. Reaching for her mother's hand, Helen, shouldered her way to a pair of empty seats to the right of the center aisle.

For the next three hours the two women witnessed extraordinary dancing. Yet while watching her competition perform their hearts out, Helen remained tranquil. She knew her craft—she knew she could compete. She had continued to train with her dance instructor, Mr. Evans regardless of her other obligations.

"Helen Thompson," a small male assistant, with a receding hairline, read from a clipboard.

Helen rose, glancing at Bertha with a small smile. A little jittery when she stepped onto the stage, the girl's dedication and discipline overrode her nerves. She posed, arms up, gracefully curved, head back, chin raised to the right, and she struck her regal beginning position. The pianist struck the opening bars, and her talent, training, and passion combined into graceful execution. Helen presented Stravinsky's Firebird—the tableau in which the Firebird rejoices over the destruction of the evil Kashchei. Her mastery of fluid motion and grace assured Helen's selection for a spot as a Gambarelli "Beauty," and she began rehearsals with a new troupe of ballerinas almost immediately after auditions.

WAR GAMES

Panama
1932-1933

A hasty mistake nearly cost young Chumbley his hard-won spot at the Pensacola flight school.

He truly loved the place—set right on Florida's balmy gulf coast. He and his fellow trainees had quickly forged a bond of comradeship, cheering each other through the daily rigor of demanding instruction. These young flyers spent most of their working hours in the cockpit, mastering landing and take-off, a maneuver called "touch-and-go."

However, the Navy kept its trainees contained until they clocked enough hours to fly solo. These novice flyers were corralled into restricted, designated training zones along the coastline. Within those limits their instructors would overlook minor errors, assessing each student's general performance per flight. All airtime was rated, and remarks typed into permanent records called "jackets."

On Chum's January, 1930 evaluation, his trainer noted, "Seaman Chumbley uses too much speed for some maneuvers, but executes them fairly well...turns and figure eights acceptable."

Reading those remarks later, Chum complained to his closest friend, Win Gardiner, "I fly any slower on those turns I'll fall in the drink."

At busy Old Corry Field in March, trainees were practicing precision landings, instructors cautioning the novices to avoid flying over specific circled areas painted on the field below. Those zones were reserved for advanced students. When Chum's turn came to take off, he casually rose about ten feet above and slightly outside one of those banned circles. At the same moment he sensed, moving past his blind spot, another plane descending, attempting a landing.

The two aircraft barely missed colliding.

A sickening sense of dread filled Chum. He pulled the stick back with his right hand, and pushed the throttle to full power with his left. He kept his wings level, as any sudden dip could catapult his plane into a fiery cartwheel.

At last, after some tense moments, the plane safely soared, leveling into smooth flight. Though the incident lasted only a flash, Chum's heart was thudding heavily. "I'll be lucky if they don't send me back to Norfolk," he fretted.

"That's a serious infraction, sailor. I will have to report it," his instructor, writing on a clipboard, coolly informed him when he'd coasted to a stop on the field. Chum hoisted himself from the cockpit, landing on legs as heavy as cement moorings.

Mortified, Chum stood rigidly at attention days later, listening to his supervisor read the official reprimand: "Any future lapses will cost you your spot at this school. Following orders is not discretionary."

"Yes, sir," the sailor faintly answered. Chum was rattled, and he got the message. He'd worked too hard to get to Pensacola to toss away his life's ambition on a thoughtless infraction. Heavy with remorse, he devoted himself even more diligently to his training, concentrating harder on flying by the book. After a while, his superiors noticed his effort, and in mid-March they placed his reprimand on hold, and ordered another flight check.

The results relieved the young pilot and pleased his instructors, who noted, "He handles the plane well and with confidence."

Thankful to have redeemed himself in the eyes of the Navy, Chum confessed to his friend, Win Gardiner, "I could never have faced my father if I loused this up."

*

Later, with his flight training securely behind him, Seaman Montgomery Chumbley received his first official orders. He and his class were assigned to Torpedo Squadron 3, located in Coco Solo, on the Atlantic coast of Panama. Chum joined his fellow novices as they shipped out southward aboard the USS Shawmont.

Watching from the deck as the Florida base vanished, the pilot silently rejoiced at this milestone. He also celebrated the fact that he didn't have to return in disgrace to Virginia. That euphoric detail made the sky somehow bluer, the clouds somehow more feathered and graceful. The young man felt nearly giddy.

After two pleasant days at sea, the Shawmont cruised into the Naval Station at Guantanamo Bay in Cuba to refuel. Chum was enchanted by the beauty of the jungle and continued to marvel at the colorful sea life and assortment of exquisite birds circling the ship for handouts. The vast horizons he used to imagine, were becoming reality.

The Squadron's final destination lay near Colon, Panama. Coco Solo was a vast, busy American naval installation, surprising the young pilot with its colossal size. The arrivals boarded a transport for delivery to their quarters, gawking out their bus windows in wonder at the enormity of the American base.

His awe continued after he and the boys were escorted to the adjacent submarine facility to tour that installation.

Returning to the field, the group sat through their initial military briefing, Chum, next to Win, listened as the instructor addressed the new aviators. The captain explained that a 1929 War Department directive assigned the US Navy the task of protecting the Atlantic zone of the Panama Canal from hostile threats.

"The Army's Fort Gulick sits adjacent to us in Coco Solo, and shares our same mission," he explained. "As some of you may already know, to the southwest, other military bases dot the entire 51 miles of the canal—all the way to where it meets the Pacific.

After the session, Chum remarked to his buddy, "I feel strangely noble defending the canal. It's as though we all are part of a bigger picture, with America expanding into both oceans."

"But what country would be nuts enough to attack us?" Win wondered.

*

War games made up much of Chum's Panama duty. The flyers were the "red" team, attacking from the air, while the "blue" team lay in wait, aboard ships "guarding" the canal. The pilots executed their orders during these simulations, but off-duty they grumbled about the Navy's outdated and seriously flawed maritime battle plans.

"I can't believe they have us flying so near enemy ships!" Chum groused, crunching over a gravel path after morning exercises. Win paced alongside as they headed toward the base canteen.

"So near? What do you mean? How else could we release our torpedoes?" His friend asked as they ordered sodas at the commissary's cafeteria.

"Think about it, Win. A torpedo aims more accurately if it detaches directly above the ocean's surface. And it's not the steep dive on approach that's fatal—it's pulling up after releasing the torpedo. That maneuver is potentially fatal. The belly of the plane is too close to enemy guns. Any surface ship could blow us to kingdom come." He smacked his palms loudly for effect.

"But, Chum, hold on! There's smoke laid down on the surface by the first two T3M's. That smoke blankets us."

"Yeah, if all goes as planned. If the smoke is laid down close enough to the water, if it doesn't rise too fast, and if the wind doesn't blow in too hard. That's a lot of ifs. Think about it. We approach in low formation, drop our payload and bank, while dangerously showing our undersides to the enemy. We'd be lucky to keep our asses dry, Win. Makes me wonder what desk genius dreamed up this idea. It's a suicide mission."

The two flyers stared at their icy drinks. Perhaps Win could see his own plane exploding into the cold depths, just as Chum had already envisioned.

"Anyhow, the scuttlebutt says the brass is taking a second look at that line of attack," Win disclosed. "The Navy wants to remodel the torpedo bombers into patrol biplanes, replacing the ordnance with fuel tanks. Can't come fast enough for me—you've made me a believer," his friend admitted.

*

Off duty, away from maneuvers and training, Chum and his buddies spent their free time out of the cockpit, and on the white and clean beaches, close to or on the base. The boys, sunning in the sand, often thanked whoever in the Department of the Navy chose such a paradise for an American outpost.

But the town was different. None of them liked going into Coco Solo with its rampant poverty, hungry, begging children, and filth. On the other hand, the Panama beaches were heaven. Chum and his buddies experimented with all the water had to offer: swimming, boating, fishing, and one wet, unsuccessful attempt at sailing.

Looking toward late spring, 1933, when his service would end, the pilot realized he was going to leave the Navy. Despite his earlier enthusiasm to make the military his career, Chum recognized he'd had his fill of taking unpredictable and arbitrary orders. He'd seen enough of Coco Solo's raggedy people and garbage-strewn roads, and enough of someone else planning his future. He had given the Navy his time, and they in turn had taught him to fly. Chum felt they were even.

His friends on base begged him to reconsider his decision.

"The commercial airlines don't give a rat's ass if you've been a military aviator," they all preached. "These companies demand a full slate of aviation licenses, Chum, and you don't have enough. No one will look at you on the outside."

With the limited time he had left in Panama, Chum moved quickly to add to his resume.

The young man ambitiously enrolled and completed a series of courses that earned him a number of specific credentials.

Though he could fix about anything, he enrolled in engine mechanics, a class that met daily in a repair hangar. Nearly always in work togs, he crawled up ladders and, covered in grease, memorized the configuration of aircraft engines.

Chum also practiced wrapping, stitching, and painting white linen strips over wood-framed fuselages and wings on biplanes. The lacquer smelled horrible, but once cured, the surface dried glassy and rigid, ready for paint.

Time was running out. By March 1933, with a scheduled departure for May, Chum included a flight navigation course, which he found quite fascinating. And finally, with a wry smile, the soon-to-be civilian enrolled in the Naval Station's radio operator course. Smiling he mumbled, "Now, Commander Seymour, I'm prepared for the future."

*

The pilot had learned a great deal about the history of commercial aviation from his Pensacola courses and from casual conversations with fellow pilots. His newfound occupation had struggled through a doubtful beginning, as private investors had tried, but failed, to make a profit from passenger transport. The overhead costs were simply out of reach for small, private operators.

However, a significant change occurred by the mid-1920s, when Congress, recognizing an opportunity to improve mail delivery, stepped in and permitted the U.S. Postal Service to contract with small air carriers. This significant federal investment sparked a rapid growth of air carriers across the country.

Pan American Airways started in South Florida, while United Airlines formed around Boise, Idaho, in the Intermountain West. Western Air Express, later renamed Transcontinental Air Transport began out of the Southwest. Chum listened carefully to the merits of each company and decided that his first choice, after he left the Navy, had to be Eastern Air Transport, out of New York City.

REALITY

New York
1933

"You're charging me import duty on my car? It's a damn Chevy! It's from *Detroit*." Chum stood with his feet apart and arms bent up as he faced the U.S. customs officer across the hood of his car, still strapped to a crane. He had arrived at the Brooklyn docks, fully expecting to drive his automobile straight into the city.

"Listen Mac," the custom's officer, burly as Paul Bunyan, explained, "The whole world's littered with American vehicles discarded after the Great War. Scrap dealers everywhere try to bring 'em in the country free, to resell here, making a big profit. So everyone forks over duty, whether your property is American made or not, including you pal."

Chum reluctantly opened his wallet. This unexpected expense put a dent in his savings and his plans, but he had to have his car for job hunting.

*

For the next two weeks the new civilian drove the streets of New York, looking for any aviation job. But he found out quickly, despite his strong background and persistence, not one company was hiring.

"We'll hang on to your resume and let you know," replayed over and over at each stop.

*

"So you've been to see all the big boys, eh?" commented a sales representative from Long Island who was seated behind a battered old desk. Airplane distributor Howard Ailor of Waco Aircraft studied the young man's face. "And by the looks of you they all turned you down."

"That is about right, Mr. Ailor." Chum responded, trying to look confident. "I was hoping you might know of something out here, maybe something at Roosevelt Field."

"I don't know you, son, but let me give you some advice. Don't dawdle around hoping for that phone call. This is no economy to sit by and wait for miracles. You'll starve first. Push your way into the air business with your own equipment, that's what I say, and I can help you with that. We have some beauties right here on site."

Chum listened to the silver-tongued salesman, surprised that he agreed with all Ailor had to say.

Chum also realized that he had returned to an America deep in the throes of financial depression.

Economic life in the 1920s had played out as a frenzied, unregulated party. By all appearances the country had embraced infinite prosperity. Insider trading and other shady practices reigned on Wall Street, where market manipulators pooled cash and bought up stock, artificially driving up values. Regular folk, believing they were on to something big, bought these tainted stocks as crooked investors dumped them, reaping fabulous profits.

Indiscriminate buying, using easy credit, pumped the overblown Dow Jones to ballooning artificial heights. Even private banks joined the frenzy, wagering the savings of their account holders to increase their own bottom line.

This facade of spreading affluence ensured the "hands off" economic policies accepted in Washington. Then the market imploded. On October 29, 1929, "Black Tuesday," the savings of a nation disappeared with the steepest financial crash in American history. Thousands upon thousands of people were ruined and the enterprise of a nation dried up.

Young Mont Chumbley had resigned from the Navy without another job, and now found there were none. The pilot's only and best assets were his optimism, his pluck, and an old Chevy.

"Over here," Ailor directed Chum, as they walked toward a hangar housing a red-with-black-trim Waco cabin biplane. "This baby's a real beauty, right? We can take it up for a spin, if you like, but you can't have this one—it's spoken for. Still cough up a down payment and we'll order you a new one. It'd be here in only six weeks.

"I came here looking for a job—and you want to sell me an airplane?" Chum blurted in disbelief.

Ailor continued to rattle on as though the pilot had not spoken. "Hell! I'm feeling generous. I'll even let you rent office space right here on Roosevelt Field for a percentage of whatever you earn as you get your footing."

Chum realized he had never encountered such a smooth operator. Ailor finally faced the boy. "Look, you can't negotiate with reality, son. And the reality is that there are no jobs. The country's flat busted."

Chum knew his mouth hung open in reaction to the salesman's bald audacity. But he also knew he agreed. Ailor was absolutely right.

Chum needed to find a way to buy that airplane. It appeared to be the only real option open to him. With little money left from his dwindling resources, he found a Western Union office and cabled his mother in Pulaski for help. He hadn't written or visited much since joining the service and felt badly his note only asked her for money. However, Martha didn't complain or hesitate.

"I'll run down to our bank in town—still solvent, doors open," she wired him right away. "A thousand, Mont? Is that enough? Where should I wire it?" Martha would still do anything to help her boy.

*

After waiting for a month and a half, filling his days with odd jobs, usually for Ailor, Chum's new airplane finally arrived at Roosevelt Field. Like a kid at Christmas, he joined the company mechanics as they checked out the Waco, making sure all the parts were intact and the plane was air-worthy.

Chum gazed lovingly at his new airplane, enchanted. It looked even sharper than the model Ailor had shown him. He wondered if the aircraft seemed so beautiful because this Waco was all his.

Painted a shiny apple red, his new purchase was trimmed with black detailing, and matching skirts covered the glossy black wheels. Anxious to get to work and begin making his payments to his mother, Chum eagerly took any flying jobs that came his way—barnstorming at county fairs, piloting passenger flights, or demonstrating new models for Howard Ailor.

His financial deliverance came, unexpectedly, only a few doors down from the Waco office.

Chum, while idling around the field, became friendly with the city boys from the press corps, chatting with these journalists as they sat outside their annex drinking sodas or smoking cigarettes. All of them worked for various news agencies: *The New York Daily News*, World-Wide Photos, and International News Photos. These information hounds collected daily only a few steps from Ailor's. A sudden ringing phone from city editors made these fellows scramble for hired planes and pilots warming up fast on the airstrip.

Though usually a convivial bunch, these men could ruthlessly turn on each other, contending for any available flyer to arrive first to accidents, natural disasters, or crime scenes. Before long Chum began to benefit from the overflowing demand. Soon, word of his availability, speed, and skill in the cockpit, brought many more knocking on Ailor's office door, looking for Mont Chumbley.

*

The young pilot negotiated his living expenses at the Essex House in Manhattan, providing air service for the hotel's exclusive clientele flying in from Connecticut or the Hamptons. In exchange for his passenger transport, Chum received his meals and a small hotel room to call home.

Planes and journalists weren't the only new features in the young pilot's life. He had met a girl—a dark haired beauty who also flew a Waco at the field. She was Frances Harrell Marsalis, one of a handful of exceptional pilots who happened to be female. Between flying his new plane, and a chance to spend some time with the enchanting Frances, Chum couldn't arrive at the field soon enough. The only drawback to Chum's new passion, the only impediment to his new infatuation—Frances was married. Torn, he couldn't find it in himself to avoid her, or pretend she didn't matter. And over time the young man told himself to settle for her company if he couldn't claim her heart.

*

On free weekends the pilot landed at rural county fairs and small town carnivals selling airplane rides—five dollars to make three passes over the fairgrounds.

One overcast, drizzly Saturday, Chum sat under the dripping wing of his plane trying to keep dry while a rain shower passed over. The fairgrounds were deserted, the weather keeping patrons at home. From his shelter, Chum watched as the carnies took refuge under striped tents and inside ticket booths.

"Does anyone want to go up for a spin? I'll do it for three bucks!" he suddenly hollered.

Carnival folks uncertainly stepped out of the gloom. Showing her bravery, the Fat Lady took the first ride, stepping off after her three passes, bursting with smiles. The Dwarf and the Strong Man flew up next, and later Chum grinned from ear to ear taking off with three clowns on board, looking out the plane's windows. This sudden inspiration earned Chum enough cash to cover gas home, dinner, and a terrific afternoon.

In early September, a *New York Times* photographer booked Chum to fly to Binghamton, New York. There had been a train wreck on the Erie Rail Line, and the cameraman was desperate to get to the wreckage.

Concerned about the weather, Chum took the fare reluctantly, knowing the flight could easily turn dangerous. Once underway, speeding northward, he watched as hazardous fog thickened around his plane. Conditions deteriorated so fast, Chum nervously told his client, "I'm going to have to put her down while I still can."

Descending through the white mist, purely on instinct, his wheels made contact hard on the field—a rough, shaking, blind landing on what turned out to be an Elmira, New York airstrip.

As Chum fought the yoke and brakes, the plane taxied too far up the landing strip, and spun with a loud "thump-bump" into a power pole, causing slight damage to the rear fuselage.

"Be back!" the cameraman shouted, unbuckling and leaping out of his seat, rushing to hire a car at the field office. Chum watched as the cameraman sped east toward Binghamton, leaving him alone to rescue his plane from the ditch. As the sky gradually cleared, and after a tractor successfully pulled the Waco from the brush and rocks, the *Times* passenger eventually returned, all smiles. The reporter had his pictures from the wreckage and was now eager to return to New York.

A week later, the Northern Pennsylvania Power Company in Susquehanna sent Chum a bill charging him $16.30 for power-line repairs in Elmira. He had already forked out cash for the work needed on his damaged plane. Disgusted, Chum swore from that day on that his plane and his livelihood were too vital for any more foolish risks.

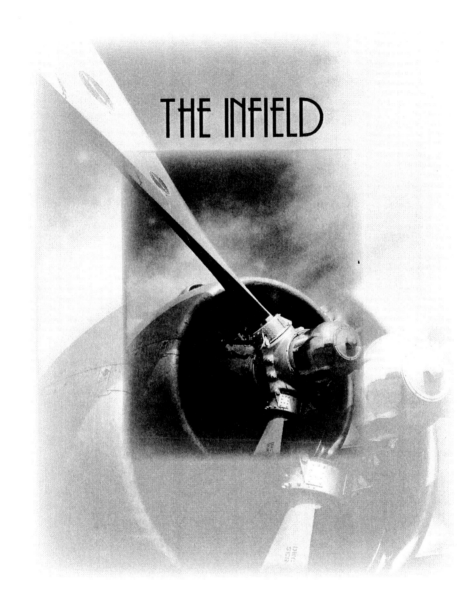

THE INFIELD

New York
1933

"You Chumbley?"

Chum glanced up from Ailor's desk, where he was adding up airtime in his logbook. A well-dressed gentleman, clearly from the city, faced him. The caller had quietly stepped through the door, surprising the pilot, intent on his figures.

"You found him, sir," Chum smiled warmly.

"My name's Rosenbaum, Richard Rosenbaum, but I go by Ross." The man extended his hand, as Chum hopped up. "Say, I need a reliable passenger plane for hire, with a good pilot at the helm. Your name was given to me over at the AP office."

"Uh huh," Chum answered casually, privately pleased at the referral. "Where exactly would you need me to fly, Mr. Ross?"

But Ross answered something else. "I have a chair on the stock exchange, but don't hold that against me," he volunteered—Chum gawked, and Ross laughed, "I know. You're surprised I have the guts to state my occupation. We Wall Street types aren't exactly popular with the public these days, are we?"

The flyer chuckled at the businessman's blunt honesty.

"Well, I won't crash the plane, if that's what worries you. The market crashing is enough for now," Chum joked back.

With the ice broken, Chum and Ross got down to business, discussing rates and various destinations. Sensing Ross could become a first-rate client, he offered, "Would you like to go up for a spin, Mr. Ross or Rosenbaum?"

The client laughed again. "Love to— love flying."

Twenty minutes later, the plane eased down, trundling to a gentle stop on the airstrip. As he released his safety straps the broker remarked, "Thanks for the test ride. You know, you're quite the pilot—may I call you Mont?"

"Nooo, sir. My friends call me Chum," the pilot answered.

"Well, Chum, I'd like you to plan on a pleasure trip next weekend. The boys and I need to get to Havre de Grace in Maryland. And I will stay in touch."

The two men shook hands again, and Ross, whistling, walked over to his Chrysler Imperial, and motored away.

Promptly a week later, while jiggling his office key into the door, Chum heard Ailor's phone ringing. He burst in, leaving the keys hanging in the lock, and seized the receiver.

"Hello, Chumbley here—hello?"

"Morning Chum," flashed an urgent voice. "This is Richard Ross, and I am awfully glad I caught you at the office! We have a horse posted in the third race and need to get to Baltimore, fast."

"Havre de Grace Race Track?"

"A horse in the third."

"Wait, where are you calling from?" the young man asked.

"Newark. We'll be waiting at the airfield for you to arrive."

"Horse track, huh? Roger that. I'll gas up the Waco and be over soon." Jogging to the hangar Chum reflected, "This trip sounds like fun, especially if I make a couple of bucks."

Taxiing down the runway, the flyer lifted off—his trip was just a short hop west—and Chum presently approached the New Jersey landing strip. From his windshield he could see three figures moving outside an office building near the tarmac.

"Must be Ross," Chum mumbled. Touching down, the pilot slowed and turned the plane toward his passengers. But he noticed they were running toward the Waco. Ross was shouting something and waving his arms.

"We need to go, now, Chum!" the pilot finally heard above his roaring engine. Chuckling, as they clambered aboard, the flyer again turned and taxied down the same airstrip, quickly lifting off toward the southeast. His three passengers breathlessly discussed the upcoming race card. Thoroughly entertained by their excitement,

Chum listened.

"That number six will be tough to beat," and "I paid a call to those stables and I wasn't that impressed."

This flight wasn't long either, but apparently too lengthy for the impatient stockbrokers. As Chum circled the county airfield, Ross reached up and patted his shoulder. "Not here, Chum. It's too far from Havre de Grace. Land the plane at the track, put it down on the infield!"

Stunned, the pilot clarified, "At the horse track?"

"Yes sir! There's no one better than you to pull off a landing like this one!"

As he doubtfully turned his plane around, dangerous images passed through Chum's mind—in particular, the incident in Elmira. He understood, as every pilot understood, that potential disaster rode along with him on every flight.

Chum worried: *What are the chances of cart-wheeling the plane? Can I regain lift if I come too close to the viewer stands? Will I be arrested?*

Ross read Chum's alarm and assured the pilot, "I trust you. The field is long enough for a good flyboy like you to manage. And we'll pay for any mishap or damage."

"How 'bout my broken neck?" the pilot half-joked.

The broker snickered.

Chum shrugged, lowered the nose of his Waco, and touched down firmly, bouncing on the grass, and smoothing out as the plane slowed. By the end of the infield, the Waco stopped, facing the viewing stands. Safe. No snags. Leaning over the yoke, he inhaled deeply realizing he'd held his breath through the approach, the landing, and the braking.

Movement in his peripheral vision caught his notice. Four race officials were rushing from under the track's white railing. The men waved their clipboards and arms over their heads, rushing toward his Waco.

Chum caught the crowd's mixed responses to his sudden appearance. Some in the crowd stood stunned, mouths hanging open, while others cheered, jumping and clapping as though his arrival was scheduled entertainment.

The pilot burst into laughter. "Now, there's the sensible crowd!" he chortled, watching as the panicked stampeded out the exits. Chum turned to tell his passengers to look at the stands, but saw that Ross had popped open the cabin door, and was dropping down from the plane.

"Take it easy, fellas. Take it easy," Ross shouted to the officials. "This pilot is the best. He does this kind of landing all the time!"

The police quickly arrived and Ross, now joined by his two associates, stood outside, as if guarding the plane. The broker talked fast, and to Chum it appeared as if the authorities were calming down, physically stepping back from the wealthy New Yorker.

Maybe they realize he's a big shot, the pilot concluded. After some tense moments the police, track managers, and officials unexpectedly shook hands with the New York businessmen, and strolled off the grass.

Hoisting himself back up into the cabin, Ross smiled. "No jail for us today, Chumbley. The track manager—the palooka in the blue blazer—only asked that you move your plane to the center of the infield, and that we stay until today's race card is finished."

Finally unhooking his safety harness, Chum stretched, climbed out of the Waco and shook his head in disbelief. He mumbled, "Tough treatment for men who live for horses."

*

"Afternoon pal, what's going on up there?"

Chum stood upon a ladder, his head buried in his plane's engine. Glancing down, he smiled. "Mr. Ross, what do you say?"

"Not much, not much. Call me Richard, will you?"

Chum laughed, "Sure Richard."

"I have an idea I want to run by you," Ross replied, looking up.

"Sure. What's on your mind? Want me to land the Waco in Yankee Stadium?" Chum teased.

"Ha. Not today, my friend. Have you heard about that night

race? Los Angeles to New York?"

"Sure have, Richard. It's the talk all over the field."

"Officially, the organizers are calling it the Darkness Derby. It opens the National Charity Air Pageant—Mrs. Roosevelt's the honorary chairman," Ross elaborated.

"All I'd heard concerning the race was $1500 for clocking in first. Boy, what I could do with all that cash," the pilot sighed.

"The cash prize isn't the half of it. Mrs. Roosevelt has many friends with deep pockets, and donations are already rolling in to go to her favorite charities."

"Well, I can only think of the one charity that has my interest—me," Chum smiled and shrugged his shoulders.

"I thought about that, too. Look, Chum. Let me make you an offer. What would you say if I loaned you the money to refit your plane for the flight? The changes would qualify your Waco for the race. If you win, you can pay me back, if you lose, I'll call it square. What do you say to that arrangement?"

Chum, astonished, asked, "On the level, Richard?"

"On the level, Chum, I owe you; and, well, I think you can win this thing."

The pilot beamed.

They closed the deal with a handshake.

Now, the young aviator had four days to retool his Waco, fly cross-country to the west coast, and find time to rest up before the official start of the race, which was slated for October 2, in Glendale California. Chum had to get moving.

Eager Waco mechanics slapped his back, shook his hand, and pulled his plane into a hangar to begin the crucial modifications. Chum could feel the electricity that permeated the repair shop, as his buddies shouted orders over the motor, propeller, fuselage, and wings—gapping plugs, and tightening bolts: one of their own was entering the Night Race.

Chum donned his own coveralls and worked his way into the plane's cabin. Kneeling, he unbolted the three unnecessary seats, installing long-range fuel tanks in their place.

"Eliminate all the excess weight you can, boys! I need this plane light."

"How 'bout the skirts over the wheels, Chum?"

"Better do it. They look good, but it's a race not a beauty pageant."

After working most of the night and into the early morning, a bleary-eyed Chum announced, "We've done all we can do fellas. I sure thank you for the help. But I need to get some sleep; I'm taking off at 5:30 tomorrow morning."

"Good Luck," hollered a mechanic. "I'll think of you as I roll over in bed."

The pilot chuckled nervously.

Instantly alert by 4:00 AM, the edgy pilot pulled on his clothes, grabbed his rucksack, and headed to the field. It was Friday morning, September 29, 1933, when Montgomery Chumbley lifted off from Roosevelt Field, in the promising light of a heartening sunrise.

Chum flew all that day above a changing landscape of warm gold and varying hues of green. Geometric angles defined farm fields, interrupted by meandering rivers that abruptly flashed in the sunlight as he passed over.

Suddenly he thought of his mother. The young aviator clearly pictured her, bent over, her purposeful fingers patiently placing tiny stitches into colorful fabric masterpieces, many of them covering the beds back home.

With some emotion, Mont realized, "She doesn't know where I am."

*

Avoiding the most rugged routes over the Rocky Mountains, Chum's path traced the upcoming derby course in reverse—from Wichita, Kansas to Albuquerque, New Mexico. He only touched down a few times to refuel the main tank. This extended, silent solitude gave Chum time to formulate a strategy to win the competition.

Pushing on through the dusky sky, he decided, *I've never flown all night—never used those airmail beacons on the ground before. Some flying tonight couldn't hurt, and I can get a feel for the dark.*

Chum's test worked out better than he hoped. Pressing west he tracked the guiding postal lights, which eventually saved him hours of flight time. He decided he'd use those signals as much as he could in the derby.

Toward morning visibility grew gradually sharper from his cockpit, and he saw the city of Los Angeles materialize below. Clusters of miniature greenery surrounded adobe colored roofs, and were dotted with azure oases of swimming pools—all connected by a labyrinth of blue-gray paved streets.

Checking his coordinates the weary pilot landed the Waco around nine at Grand Central Air Terminal in Glendale. Chum noted droves of people gathered around office fronts and hangars flanking the runway, as he slowed the plane to a crawl.

They're here for the race, he thought.

Taxiing toward the Waco hangar, Chum steered his plane with extra care around the wandering crowds, concerned with testing his drained reflexes.

"Hey Chum, how was the trip?" asked a pleasant Waco representative greeting him as he stepped off the plane.

"Long. I'm a little worn," Chum extended his hand.

"I'm Bill Merriman. Howard cabled yesterday telling me to expect you," the company representative answered.

"I could use a little sleep, Bill. Are any hotels near that are decent, and reasonable?"

"Oh, no. None of that. You are Waco's guest of honor. Got a room waiting for you here, behind my office. All the comforts of home. And Chum, there are reporters and photographers everywhere. If you want sleep—you'd better disappear, fast."

Chum's nod quickly turned into a deep yawn.

Shifting around in the squeaky, narrow bed, Chum knew he was too worked up to rest. He soon gave up trying and wandered back to the hangar. Squatting, he began a thorough equipment check on his airplane.

"Tires look okay," he noted, thumbing the tread.

"Landing gear seems solid," he concluded grasping a strut.

Next he lifted the engine cowling and swiftly eyed the motor.

"Plugs, prop belt, and pistons look good, too. Boys did a good job."

Inside the cabin he checked the new fuel clamps and found them secure. "Good."

Relieved, the pilot returned to the cot and slept soundly.

LES GIRLS

Europe
1932

Bertha answered a light knock on the door of the Whitby apartment, where a young man in uniform and cap smiled in greeting. He handed her a thin yellow and blue envelope.

"Telegram for Miss Helen Thompson," the boy announced.

Bertha fingered the note, as Helen strolled up. "What is it, B?"

"Get a coin, will you?"

Helen rummaged in Bertha's purse at a side table and returned to the door, handing the courier a nickel.

"Thank you," she said quickly, as her mother latched the door. "Who's it for?"

Bertha had already inserted her thumb under the seal of the cable but Helen's face, wide-eyed and childlike, stopped her.

"It's for you," she admitted, and reluctantly handed the cable to her daughter.

Helen unfolded the telegram. Her face instantly changed from benign, to stunned, to worried.

"What's the matter, Helen? Who is it from?"

"Grant's finally divorced." Helen passed the envelope to Bertha, but the paper floated to the floor as Helen absently turned away.

Shaking her head in disgust, Bertha scooped up the telegram and read, *Darling, hurry home—divorced now. Love from now on. Gee.*

"That scoundrel! How dare he contact you now, and here at my home?"

Helen flitted to the window, pushed aside the sheers, and gazed onto busy 45th Street.

"I can't believe his nerve!" Bertha fumed, closely eyeing her daughter.

But the girl barely heard her mother. She idly watched a newsboy hawking papers on the street corner as she mused, *it's only two more days until I sail. My departure must have pushed Grant into action. Whatever his divorce means, I've signed my contract and have to go. I want to go. I guess Grant will have to wait for me this time.*

Bertha fluttered nonstop around Helen. She fussed with the girl's hair, washed and ironed her clothes, sorted, and then resorted Helen's trunk—she even painted the girl's toe nails, seeming afraid to let go of her foot.

"If you rush to California, to Grant, instead of sailing to Europe, you'll make the biggest mistake of your life. I won't allow it!" Bertha repeatedly told Helen. "You have a chance to be somebody. Don't let that no-account idler ruin our plans!"

Helen's repeated assurances gave her no peace. Bertha, fatigued with worry, finally exhaled heavily into her chair. Glancing to the end table next to her, she spied the tri-folded Gambarelli contract. Bertha picked up the document and reread a portion of her daughter's extraordinary contract once again.

> *Henry Lartique of the Lartique Agency at 39 Avenue des Champs-Elysees, Paris, in conjunction with the William Morris Agency of New York, and Helen Thompson, dancer, of 425 45th Street, New York, have reached mutual terms for a tour to begin March 25th 1932.*

Still Bertha continued to fret, and she dreaded her girl traveling so far away from home. Helen's impending departure triggered old sorrows that refuse to heal.

It was summer, August of 1925, when her husband, Floyd Thompson died unexpectedly, in his bed. The luckless showman had been exhibiting signs of fatigue, hobbling a little slower, seeming more lethargic than usual. It wasn't long before he remained in bed all day, quite odd for the usually effervescent Floyd Thompson. He passed off his weariness, claiming all he needed was a little rest. And it was in that bed that his wife later found him, struggling for breath, rattling air erratically into his failing lungs.

Bertha had quickly summoned a doctor, but there was nothing to do. Floyd was past any help. His wife, his two daughters, and a physician stood by, powerless to save him. Unbearable heat hung in the stifling room, as Floyd's body gradually grew cold. Bertha was frozen, as well, refusing to accept that her husband, like her mother before, had deserted her. Her unbearable pain resurfaced, and again, the little girl within grieved beyond any solace.

Those she loved most always left her.

*

Bertha eventually recovered when she recalled the threat of Grant Garrett and Los Angeles. A satisfied Mrs. Thompson bid Helen and *The American Beauties* farewell, as the girls waved enthusiastically from the ship's gangway. The S.S. *Ile de France* weighed anchor for an Atlantic crossing, Saturday, April 30, 1932.

Watching from the docks, Bertha knew, despite having to say goodbye, she had saved her baby from an unworthy man who was bent on stealing her Helen away.

*

Dear Mother,

When we left the harbor the purser ushered us to our berths in second class, down a floor from the top deck, but then— surprise!—handed us passes to first class. He told us to come up any time we wanted for motion pictures and dancing.

Today, sitting among first class passengers and crew, we watched a screening of Greta Garbo in "Mata Hari," which was much better than the silent instructional films with French and English subtitles showing below. Each afternoon, all the girls in the company take tea in the Grand Salon, and return in the evening for orchestra concerts and dancing. Mother, I've never seen such elegance—you were right about bringing my evening gowns!

I can't begin to describe the décor. A vast floral carpet centers an enormous sitting area, surrounded by at least 60 upholstered chairs. Wall murals of clouds and trees decorate the grand staircase, lit by a huge crystal chandelier. Such sophistication! Smaller chandeliers are suspended in every lobby throughout the ship, where wainscoting and gold-flecked paper cover the walls, and vases of fresh flowers sit on polished side tables! Wherever we wander, passengers lounge around, to talk, sip tea, or play cards.

I share a cabin with two of the girls in the show, Grace and Charlotte—we pal around everywhere. Their mothers live in New York, too, and I'm sure you'll like them when you meet them. I'm on the top deck writing this and need to stop for now. It's time to go down for dinner.

8:00 PM

It has turned out that everyone in our party is stricken with seasickness— except me. I enjoyed my pork loin tonight and strolled around after the dinner.

I've tried not to be smug, but Miss Gambarelli, ill in her stateroom, marveled at my "iron" constitution. I explained to poor Grace, flat on her back in our cabin, that I decided not to become sick and my resolve saves me from it. I owe this trip to you and wish you were here to share it with me.

Your loving daughter,
Little Helen

My Darling Helen,

New York is dull without you. Even with clear skies and the park in springtime bloom, I feel blue. It will be nice when you come home.

Your loving mother

Dear Mother,

Our ship arrived in Le Havre via Plymouth, England, and now we're on a train bound for Paris! I'm so excited to see the city. All the girls are. We promised each other to visit the Eiffel Tower! Sorry my writing is such a mess, but this railcar is riding rough! We're stumbling up and down the aisle with the constant lurching, and I can barely keep this pencil on the paper. I've watched the rolling countryside out the window until it became too dark to see anything. I will write more when the train smoothes out.

1:30 AM!

Events careened out of control once we arrived in Paris, and I haven't had a moment to breathe.

Our train finally pulled in to Gare Sainte Lazare Station, in the center of Paris. Miss Gambarelli ordered us to "Hurry ladies, hurry!" as we found our luggage tossed like potato sacks from the baggage car. Next she shouted, "Our taxis await!"

The woman sounded like a bad movie. If we hadn't been so pooped we would have laughed. The caravan of taxis got us to the hotel—but not for long. There weren't enough rooms for all of us. And Mother, the rain cascaded down on us in an icy spray, (and it was so late and cold, poor Carmen dissolved into tears).

Soon Gambarelli ordered us back to the cabs for another ride to the Hotel Rovaro, a larger establishment. We were all soaked, numb and exhausted.

The good news is, though small, our rooms at the Rovaro have high ceilings and rectangular windows from ceiling to floor. It makes the space seem bigger. But best of all there are warms beds! That made all of us feel better. But I'm worn out now, and my legs are still wobbly from the train ride. I'll write more in the morning.

11:30 AM

Charlotte, Grace, and I decided to share our little room, since we bunked together on the ship. We've also decided to share expenses to cover rent and food, and we take turns shopping at a nearby market. That way, we can hopefully save a little money.

We've begun rehearsals already at the Les Ambassadeurs Dinner Theatre for our debut, and we'll perform at the theater for four weeks. The bellman told us the club is elegant, and Miss Gambarelli says it attracts only the most refined Parisians, along with distinguished foreign clientele. After her talk, I felt my first butterflies about the engagement!

Cheer up, Bert. I don't want to worry about you.

Yours truly,
The World Traveler

Dearest daughter,

Your adventures sound exciting. I'm sure you'll perform wondrously. Eileen is home, which is nice. Remember not to go off alone! It isn't safe.

Your devoted mother

Dearest B,

Mr. Lartique made some changes to our troupe title. On the marquee, we're no longer "Beauties" but "Les Girls."

Though Miss Gambarelli still is the headliner, her name still embossed in gold on the marquee, and again in the playbill, she was clearly unhappy with his interference. Her opening solo is breathtaking—a piece from Giselle. But you'll never guess—I've been given a solo, too! I take the stage during a set switch, while the girls catch their breath and change their toe-shoes.

I found a billowy silk blouse and matching skirt, and a deep blue velvet fitted vest. I perform that acrobatic Rhapsody

in Blue number with the walkovers and the audience gasps watching the flips and leaps en point. The applause is magical!
Helen

Oh, Mother!

We're all so frustrated here. Miss Gambarelli has become so difficult and critical, despite the quality of our rehearsals. We've done nothing differently, yet all we hear her say is "No, no. Do it correctly this time." Or "You clumsy girls! You will never be ready."

We didn't know what to think. Then we heard rumors. One of the stage managers told another dancer, Lillian, that Gamby is unhappy with her relationship with Mr. Lartique. She apparently thinks she's not getting everything specified in her contract. And we are the ones paying by suffering through her sour moods. As soon as she enters the room, the tension swells like a balloon threatening to pop. More later, Bert—the girls want me to go to the market with them.

6:30 PM

And pop it did. Lartique fired Gamby! We now have lost our headliner and wonder what will become of us. We all want to continue the tour because Lartique has already booked standing engagements across Europe. Please don't worry Mother, I am safe. We've paid our rent through the week. I will keep you posted.

How are you holding up?
H.

Dear Mother,

We have traveled on to sunny Monte Carlo, without our star. The show goes on, right? I'm performing my solo and we all perform in two other pieces in place of Gamby's spots. Mr. Lartique insisted that we complete the tour, and that should bring me home around the end of September if nothing else come through.

You can't imagine how the very rich live and play here on the Riviera. These people own lavish homes perched on a steep rocky incline. We all hiked to a high, scenic, spot and the view was spectacular. The Mediterranean, azure-blue sparkled below, the bay full of sailboats, motorboats, and fancy yachts, plus swimmers in colorful bathing suits. I wore some new white sandals with wedged heels and laces that wrap up my ankle. Very cute—but not for walking up such a rough, rocky rise.

Every day before rehearsal, we meander around the resort, meeting local people and trying to make conversation with them. Somehow, it must work, because we've had invitations to go walking, boating, and swimming. Don't worry—the boys are very respectful.

Oh, you won't believe this, but our show's name has changed again! Now we are billed as "Les 11 Beautes' Americaines." So we lost our headliner and gained a new name. Nothing on this trip surprises me anymore.

We are opening at a new casino here called the Terminus Hotel. The manager arranged for the dance company to pose for publicity photos, which we saw later in a glossy Monte Carlo magazine. The camera crew asked us to pose in our bathing suits around the hotel pool, dressed in our costumes on stage, and on a balcony overlooking the water. The opening night is July 29.

Mother, I'm sorry I haven't sent any money. Because of Gambarelli's lawsuit against Mr. Lartique, we haven't received our usual pay. But we just learned he's sending a stipend of $20 each for our food and hotel bills. This situation is temporary, so please cheer up and don't worry.

On a brighter note, our ballet company will still play in Erba, Italy at the end of September. Remember? Lartique *contracted that engagement back in New York for us to dance in a production of Goethe's Faust. I can't wait to see Italy!*

Your dutiful daughter,
Helen

Helen,
Well, we shall have to tighten our belts here and limp along, so don't you worry either. Did you actually need new sandals? You should watch your spending. We look forward to seeing you back in New York after Erba.

Mother

A FRENCH LEGEND

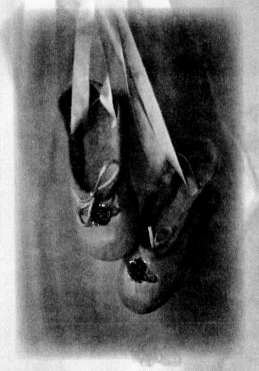

Monte Carlo
1932

Events, however, kept Helen from returning to New York after the Faust performance. She, along with her fellow dancers, was delighted to find they were remaining in Europe. The troupe's deliverance arrived with the appearance of a famous French dancer and music hall entertainer, the iconic Mistinguett.

While she was on holiday in the fashionable resort, "Miss" as her admirers affectionately called her, caught the American troupe's Terminus Hotel performance. Impressed by the quality of the production, the choreography, and the expertise of the ballerinas, Miss decided to hire them.

Returning to the theater the following afternoon, the French entertainer came upon Les Girls rehearsing on stage.
"Pardon, pardon," she interrupted. The pianist, hearing her first, stopped playing, and the girls turned to see why. Miss then invited the puzzled dancers to sit in the first row, and she began to clarify her business in hesitant English.

"Currently I am organizing a new revue to host across the continent. After attending your wonderful performance last night, I am convinced that all of you would work well in my new company."

The girls were silent for a moment, while the woman's words sunk in, and then all spoke at once, chattering excitedly. Mistinguett smiled at the girls' reaction, pleased at their enthusiasm, until Lillian let loose with a shrill, All-American, two-fingered whistle. Quieting the room, Lillian then turned toward the grand lady explaining, "Ma'am, we would love to join you. But our contracts are with the Lartique Agency in Paris, and it would be up to Mr. Lartique."

"Very well, my dear. I will cable your Mr. Lartique in Paris promptly."

*

The talented French-born songstress had enjoyed a devoted following for decades, with sold-out performances and enthusiastic audiences who often sang along and applauded their favorite numbers. Many evenings the crowds rose from their seats in appreciative ovation to their favorite Mistinguett dance pieces and beloved songs. In particular, Mistinguett's signature torch song, *Mon Homme*, could move her faithful audiences to tears. The ballad became popular on both sides of the Atlantic, memorably recorded in English by Fanny Brice with her rendition of "My Man" in the Ziegfeld Follies.

By the time of her Monte Carlo holiday, Miss, though now an aging dowager of the stage could still draw large, loyal crowds wherever the headliner appeared.

Miss quickly received authorization to offer the abandoned ballet troupe a new contract to continue their tour with her, beginning in October, 1932. The star gathered the Beauties together for a second meeting in the Terminus lobby to explain the girls' options.

"First of all, I am delighted to welcome you to my new production, "Voila Paris." However Mr. Lartique requires that I inform you, if you should choose to return to the United States following the Erba performance, the agency will pay your expenses home. But I most ardently hope you decide to remain with me on the continent. My dears, I shall accompany you on a most memorable journey across Europe.

With that said I hope we will soon share the stage together, and that all of you will bear testament to Europeans that Americans share in the exquisite art of classical dance. I shall give you until tomorrow afternoon at 5:00 PM to sign your copy of the new agreement." Mistinguett smiled warmly at the ballerinas and left the hotel.

At first no one spoke. The dancers simply blinked and looked at one another. Then Carmen declared, "I'm staying."

"I need the money," echoed Lillian.

While Helen watched, all the girls publicly affirmed their intentions. When all eyes turned toward her, she spoke without hesitation. "Well, I guess I'm staying to bear testament that Americans can do whatever it was she said we can do."

The Beauties had to laugh at her sarcasm. For Helen, returning to New York so soon would have felt like failing—she was anxious to resume her adventure and see more of Europe.

*

"Rumor has it that Mistinguett served as a spy for the French government during the Great War while she was dancing across the continent. They may be watching her again because of that new leader in Germany," Lillian remarked as the company sunned themselves on exclusive Larvotto Beach.

"Who told you such a thing, Lillian?" Una, another dancer, asked skeptically.

"Didier, the older stage manager at the Terminus—he seems to know all about Miss."

Charlotte's eyes grew large. "How thrilling!"

"And she's had many affairs with younger men," Lillian continued, enjoying the attention. "You're familiar with Maurice Chevalier?"

"Of course."

"Supposedly they shared a passionate, very public romance. Miss launched his career when she plucked him from a music hall chorus line and cast him into his first film, *La Valse Renversante.*"

"No!" Charlotte blurted.

"Oh, yes!"

"Isn't he a lot younger?"

"Thirteen years, according to Didier."

"Lucky woman!" Charlotte said. The rest of the girl's laughed at her response.

Despite her storied reputation, the Mistinguett Helen came to know fell far short of her legend. The woman walked slightly hunched over, with her step not quite as agile as it must have been in her younger years. But incredibly enough, when Miss stood under the spotlight, a miraculous transformation took place. Her full voice still filled halls with magnificent authority, and her powerfully magnetic presence left audiences, cast, and crew utterly spellbound.

Yet, the grand dame's daily face revealed a grittier side. At the Austrian border, as their train stopped for a crossing check, custom officials required each performer to pay a working fee to enter the country. The lauded entertainer was suddenly seen gazing out her carriage window, as though interested in the countryside. The dancers weren't fooled. Miss was stalling, hoping the girls would pay their own fees—but the Americans joined ranks, all glaring meaningfully at the headliner. Finally, Miss, "tsk-ing" in disgust, dug into her pocketbook and reluctantly doled out the required currency.

Dear Mother,

We were paid today, and I marched straight to the American Express office to send you a money order. I am sorry it's only $50, but I had to buy another pair of walking shoes. The pair I brought in Monte Carlo gave out near Schonbrunn Palace in Vienna. We were on a walking tour when my right heel caught a crack in the street—and pop! It was gone. I had to hop back to our hotel, one hand on Charlotte's shoulder. We looked so funny hobbling down the street.

I promptly found a shoe shop and bought a new pair, reasonably priced. The new ones are very cute— tan sandals with a strap around the ankle.

Don't worry about me, I didn't hurt myself. Only the worn-out shoe suffered. I am eating well and working hard. We all stick together when we leave our hotel, and no one has dated any of the boys who follow us around. So, don't worry, I am minding my Ps and Qs. I'll send more money on my next payday.

Love,
Me

Dearest Bert,

Sorry I haven't written for a bit. We have been pushed from pillar to post! I hardly have time to breathe with our traveling schedule.

But I do have a check on the way to New York. I try to send money through the American Express offices. But, now that we are outside of Paris, I have to find a bank, exchange the francs, lira, marks—whatever, into dollars. Then I must find a post office to send the money home as registered mail.

I want to let you know I had to have my hair done and polished my nails for our opening tomorrow night. I also bought new gloves and a blue dress—but I needed them. My other blue dress is threadbare. Do you remember it? I've had it for ages.

Guess who I spied at our show in Marseilles? Marie Dressler, who recently won an Academy Award! She was seated next to Earl Carroll, the Broadway director!

I'm so sorry the money's been short. We Beauties incur a number of expenses you might not expect, just to stay beauties.

Has the employment situation improved at all in New York? Anything opening for dancers? I'm so relieved this European tour came along to keep us from the poorhouse.

I miss you and Eileen so much! Thank you, Bert, for allowing me this grand adventure. I've gained so much in skill and professional experience.

However Mother, you just say the word and I'll come back home.

I want to finish this to post, before the S. S. Bremen sails to New York.

> As always,
> Your loving daughter,
> Helen

Helen,

Yes, it must feel wonderful for you, shopping and sightseeing while your sister and I scrape for every crumb. Do you imagine our clothes have not become threadbare? Did it cross your mind to find a shoe repair shop for that broken heel? I suppose you may waste your summer in Europe, as you've requested. God knows no jobs await you here.

Mother

*

Miss decided to rename the American dance troupe yet again, now that they worked exclusively for the French legend. Helen and her fellow troupers were now called the "Ambassadeurs Beauties Americaine."

This new Mistinguett production, *Voila Paris,* featured a diversified program adding other dance ensembles and singers, creating a multi-talented cavalcade.

Others in the Voila playbill included, an American male dance line, "Earl Leslie *et ses* Boys," a female vocalist called simply "Fraisette," solo dancer, Topsi Hall, and the singing-dancing Dore' Sisters. Helen felt this new tour was an exciting change from the all-girl company of eleven ballerinas.

*

"Whose name is on the note?" Helen whispered to her friend. She and Charlotte had been the first dancers through the dressing room door after their final curtain, and discovered a colorful bouquet. Charlotte turned the tiny envelope back from the baby's breath, and murmured, "It says Lillian."

The rest of the company swarmed into the cluttered room, talking over each other while mopping their foreheads with small flannel towels.

"What a grand audience." Lillian smiled.

"Did you hear those boys shouting at us? Shouting at ballet!" Grace added in disbelief.

"What's this? Wait a minute—where did these flowers come from?" Lillian demanded.

"We have no idea who sent them, honest, Lil. They were already here when we came in," Charlotte explained. Glaring at the spray and without any hesitation, Lillian Ward dropped the flowers and the card into the trashcan. "Well whoever they're from, I can't accept them. My Douglas wouldn't approve."

"Aaah, Lil!" Charlotte whined. Lillian ignored her friends as she sat down and spread cold cream on her cheeks. Helen took one last look at the flowers resting in the trashcan wondering if anyone would ever be moved enough by her performance to send flowers.

*

Booked at the Palace Hotel in Brussels, the show's new variety lineup fused seamlessly. First the star, Mistinguett, with the ballet troupe opened the evening program. Helen, unable to dance both with her friends and in her solo, chose the latter. Happily, it became a crowd favorite. Though she would have liked to dance with the company, Helen knew the ovations she garnered were well worth watching the opening from the wings. Next on the bill was synchronized dancing from American Earl Leslie and his line of hoofers, followed by the other company entertainers and their specialties.

The program closed with the full cast in a colorful, peacock-inspired, extravaganza. It featured Mistinguett center-stage, supporting a headdress of colossal feathered plumes of blue, turquoise, and purple, shimmering above her blonde hair. Her "Beauties" were costumed in silvery tutus, sequined halters, and tight, sparkling caps, each sprouting oversized silver feathers, flanking their star from both sides.

The male dancers, in black tuxedos, peeked out between each feathered girl. Under the dazzling lights, the symmetrical tableau moved patrons to their feet, applauding and shouting for more.

For a second night more flowers appeared, and this time a note accompanied the gift on Lillian's dressing room table. As she again picked up the vase and turned toward the trash bin, Carmen stopped her, "At least read the note first, Lillian."

"Yeah Lil, c'mon!" the other dancers chanted.

"Who wrote it?" asked Grace.

"Is it signed?" wondered Carmen.

Rolling her eyes, the dancer huffed dramatically, then slit open the note with a nail file and read in a flat, monotone:

> *You were really wonderful in your solo specialty and all through the review and I do want once again to ask you if you will let me pilot you through town in my car when and for as long as you may care. Should you not care to see or know me, please allow these flowers to tell you of my admiration, and remember that you have a person who cares for you in the little city of Brussels.*

"But I didn't have a solo," Lillian exclaimed. "The only one who had a solo was..."

The girls stood silently, and then all eyes shifted to Helen. Lillian laughed once—a bit annoyed, and handed the vase to her friend, saying, "I believe these belong to you."

Banter erupted again, now aimed at Helen.

"Jeepers girl, he admires you!" and "Wonder who it is that cares for you in this little city, kid?"

Helen took their teasing in stride, curtsying and blowing kisses. But when the dancers began chatting about the imminent cast party, Helen lowered herself onto a rickety stool and read on. "I feel I must say that I am not an 'old butter and egg man' ... I am just twenty-eight and not too ugly... My only fault is that I think you are my ideal."

Her eyes lingered on the words "my ideal." Unexpectedly charmed, Helen appraised this communiqué with new eyes, and decided to follow the mysterious sender's written instructions on how and where to meet him.

Helen hurried out of the dressing room, heaving open the steel stage door into the quiet alley behind the theatre.

Stepping to the corner of the building, she peeked around to the snow-lined, busy street. Helen carefully studied the faces of the bundled up after-theatre crowd crunching by, and scrutinized moving and parked automobiles. From her vantage point, she soon spied a grey Packard, emitting white-blue exhaust from a quietly idling engine. Scanning the note again, Helen felt certain that the young man would be waiting in that car. Her stomach faintly roiling, she stepped forward, trying to distinguish the driver through his frosty door window.

Helen realized, *oh, he looks nice*, and shyly continued to approach his vehicle. The driver stepped out of his door, all smiles.

"You must be Lillian," he beamed, "I am Elie. Elie Gelaki," he added, bowing to kiss Helen's gloved hand. She noticed that the young man's voice formally articulated his clear English.

She bashfully smiled and felt her face grow warm. "Actually, I'm Helen," she clarified. "I do hope that I am the one the message was meant for..."

Elie Gelaki unexpectedly gazed at her forcefully. "I meant you."

The two stood self-consciously beside the running automobile. "Why don't I take you inside this café? It is quite cold tonight."

"That would be lovely, Mr. Gelaki," Helen smiled, more relaxed.

The young man gently took hold of her arm, smiling, "I'm Elie, and this street is quite icy." He courteously escorted the dancer into a nearby coffee house.

"So you are the Helen Thompson on the bill, not Lillian Ward," he said after they were seated. "I am sorry about the confusion. I hope it was of no embarrassment to you."

"No more than usual," the dancer laughed. "My friends spend more time teasing each other than dancing." She paused, changing the subject. "Tell me about yourself, Elie."

"I am a native of Palestine. But now I live here, in Brussels, with my mother and two sisters. My dear father has been for dead for some time." He noticed Helen suddenly frown. "Did I say something offensive?"

"No. I'm sorry. My father died some years ago, too." Helen's own grief abruptly gripped her heart. After Floyd Thompson died, after his funeral, she knew something truly good had vanished forever from her world.

Her frown turned into a sympathetic smile. His face glowed in reply. Elie changed the subject. "I have recently founded a new photo company. I call it Polyfoto International," he stated proudly. "At this time I am expanding my interests in Europe, across North America, and on into Asia.

"What type of photography do you specialize in?" Helen politely asked.

"I will accompany you into my studio and photograph your lovely face," he answered with assurance. "Then you will know."

While he chatted about his life and work, Helen studied the Belgian. He wasn't terribly tall, and had a clear complexion, subtly suggesting a childhood of freckles. His thick hair ranged from light brown to dark blonde and he combed it back off of his forehead. Elie gazed at her from olive green eyes speckled with glints of brown and gold. Though he seemed a serious man, he smiled broadly as he spoke in his appealing English, and his laughter was deep and friendly.

"Would you consider joining me for lunch tomorrow?" he asked. "I would be happy to guide you on a personal sightseeing tour of the city afterward."

"Love to," she answered promptly, drawn toward this young man. Elie thanked her with a happy grin.

The troublesome doubt dawned on her later, as she tiptoed into her dark hotel room.

"He's Jewish," she whispered to herself. "My mother would just die if she knew I was seeing a Jew."

Yet, despite all the prejudice against Jewish people, she liked Elie and decided to give the young man a chance. He seemed nice, and she wanted to see the sights around Brussels.

A CULTURED GENTLEMAN

Europe
1932

After Brussels, Elie visited nearly every town Helen played, frequently heralding his arrival with a spray of flowers waiting for her at each hotel.

"Please, please invite your friends to join us on our outing," Elie cheerfully encouraged Helen.

In Paris, where *Voila* was performing, Elie motored a carload of Beauties to the countryside, stopping at the Bourbon Palace of Versailles. The American girls strolled amid the recovering gardens, the graceful flowing fountains, and grand buildings that had been severely neglected during the Great War, not so long before.

"Elie, this place is magical!" Helen exclaimed. "Have you been here before?"

"Only once," the young man replied. "We—my mother, two sisters and I, traveled to Paris after the funeral of my father in northwest France. Perhaps I will take you up there another time."

They toured the ornate grand salons including Marie Antoinette's *Petit Trianon*, the queen's palace. Helen lost herself, dazzled with the elaborate ivory and gold friezes along the walls and ceilings, and the gold-framed paintings hung in arched cornices.

Later, standing before a vast mirror in the Hall of Mirrors, the couple caught their reflection together—Elie smiling tenderly while Helen felt an inexplicable pang of regret.

In Strasbourg, on another day trip, the pair enjoyed a 12:00 tour of the town's beautiful Gothic cathedral.

"Oh!" Helen exclaimed, captivated by the cathedral's ornate astronomical clock inside the transept.

Elie whispered, "Wait my dear, it gets better."

After only a few moments, small figurines emerged from above the blue and gold clock, within a square opening of the sandstone wall. The carvings represented the phases of life, holy saints, and culminated with statuettes of Jesus and his twelve apostles. While absorbed in the intricacy of the synchronized whirring, Helen felt a touch on her hand, as Elie took her arm. Together, the two silently contemplated this majestic tribute to the Almighty's dominion over time.

On another stop Elie caught up with Helen by driving to Geneva. In the morning, before rehearsals, the Belgian escorted the dancer on a visit to the League of Nations.

"How did you manage passes, Elie? Charlotte and Grace were told they needed a sponsor to attend," Helen whispered in the vast paneled halls, watching Elie retrieve the official cards from his pocket.

"I have a business contact here in the city who agreed to endorse us," Elie quietly responded.

Finding their seats in the public gallery, Helen listened as one prominent gentleman after another eloquently spoke of a peaceful world. Moved by the solemn atmosphere in the chamber, the dignified proceedings, and the sincerity of all the delegates' remarks, she whispered to her new friend, "These men sound determined to spare the world from another war."

"My dearest girl, I truly hope they are successful," Elie answered emotionally, gazing at the proceedings with brimming eyes.

*

Elie was in London on business, unable to attend Helen's ballet performance in Erba, a town in northern Italy which was a holdover obligation from the Gambarelli contract. Mistinguett permitted the rest of the cast time off while the girls rehearsed for the somber ballet—Goethe's *Faust*. This dark saga, a morality tale of the man who sold his soul to the devil for worldly power, puzzled the ballerinas.

"Ballet is a serious dance form, it's true," complained Una, "but this performance is so grim, I'll bet there's no belly laughs, or knee slappers in the aisles tonight."

A murmur of assent echoed in the dressing room.

*

The cast party after the program proved to be anything but grim or serious. Accompanied by two Italian boys, Eddie and Nikko— young men the dancers had met earlier—the crowd left the theater in a cacophony of chatter and laughter.

Parading to a nearby café, the American girls swarmed around small tables on the stone terrace. Under a garland of dim light bulbs strung around the courtyard, clouds of rising blue cigarette smoke, laughter, and chinking glasses animated the softly lit oasis, the celebration flowing easily against the night.

"Have you tasted cognac, Miss Helene?" Nikko asked, in an innocent tone.

"No, Nikko. It's bourbon for this girl."

"My dear, cognac is the nectar of the heavens. You must try a sip."

Helen reluctantly stared at the cognac the Italian pushed in front of her. She cautiously raised the snifter, appraised the aroma warily, and sipped. Choking a bit, she concluded, "This isn't bad."

Nikko, grinning, ordered another. The more cognac she consumed, the more earnestly the dancer explained how she was properly instructed to perform Ballet spotters back in New York. Eddie sat, enchanted, listening to the pretty American girl. He suddenly asked, "Lovely Helene, would you permit me the privilege of observing your spotters?"

Nikko winked at his friend, and then added, "I have never seen a New York spotter."

"Go on, Helen, show us how your Mr. Evans says it should be done," egged on Grace, weaving unsteadily around the table to watch.

"New York spotters!" demanded several voices. Looking blearily around at her audience, Helen wobbled to her feet. The little crowd applauded.

"Hop up on the table, Helen. We can't see your footwork from here," shouted Carmen. Helen warily looked at the tabletop. She carefully placed her knee onto the edge, testing its strength, and satisfied it wouldn't tip or collapse, awkwardly clambered up.

She clumsily rose to her toes. Lightheaded from the alcohol, the dancer tried to focus on a fixed spot, but just couldn't pinpoint one. One rotation she turned, then another, and Helen began to gather speed. Inevitably, and all too soon, the girl tottered, losing her footing and equilibrium. Luckily for her, spectators surrounded the table and as she listed at a dangerous angle, the boys caught her before she hit the unforgiving flagstones.

Sick and sore the next morning, the no-longer-graceful ballerina retching in the bathroom, gasped, "Nectar for the gods? Tasted more like lighter fluid. I—hate—everyone."

*

Elie caught up with the Mistinguett Company when Helen and her friends returned to Paris. Pleased to be reunited with the lovely American girl, he offered the group another afternoon tour in his Packard.

"I have my automobile, and you can decide our destination," he invited.

"We've been to The Louvre." Carmen mentioned.

"I loved the Mona Lisa, remember, Helen?" added Charlotte.

"The Winged Victory was wonderful, too. Plus we have visited the Arch de Triomphe and the Eiffel Tower," Helen finished. "I think that today it's your choice, Elie."

The Belgian looked the girls over, gazing mostly at Helen. "I believe I have an idea. Climb in. We will motor north."

The party journeyed under a cloudless blue sky to the northeast. Eventually, after passing through some small villages, Elie veered onto a narrow road, parking his Packard in a field.

"This is the battle area known as the Marne," he announced soberly.

The girls quietly climbed out of his vehicle almost reverently at the familiar name of the legendary site. The young man guided the group over the ribbons of scarred landscape left by the many futile attacks that made up the Marne Campaign in the Great War.

"Was your father killed here, Elie?" Helen whispered. "No, Helen, he died later, further northwest near the Somme River. That is where he is buried."

It wasn't a topic she gushed over in her letters to New York. That afternoon excursion made the wreckage of war too real for a dancer from faraway America.

*

Back in Paris Helen was astonished to find a letter postmarked from Los Angeles, California. Grant's letter seemed from another world, another lifetime. Helen slowly opened the envelope and read,

> *My Dearest Little Nell*
> *As you can see I am still residing in the City of Angels. Your silence took the starch out of a booking to South America and I took a pass. I am waiting patiently for my partner to return from her world travels. Shall play nary a date till you arrive... will continue to play my hunches instead... and never doubt me even when I am not with you.*

Below his note, Grant had sketched a whimsical map of the routes he planned to book for her return.

He cleverly illustrated the stops with leaning snowy mountains in Denver, oversized, smiling cactus in Phoenix, and swaying skyscrapers back in New York.

"Oh Grant Garrett, you are a charmer, and I do miss you," she murmured, feeling a little sentimental.

"Helen, did you say something?" Grace asked, glancing up from her bed.

"Oh—no. Sorry, Grace. I didn't mean to wake you," the girl murmered.

Lying back on her pillow she mused, *I can hardly believe it, but Grant hasn't crossed my mind since I sailed in April. The tour has been so fast and so thrilling. For now,* she yawned, *I'm just glad to be here. I'm far enough away from those who spend all of their time planning my life.*

LONGING FOR HOME

1933

Dearest Bert,

We have boarded the El Kantara for our crossing of the Mediterranean Sea. Voila is booked to play in both Tunis and Algiers in North Africa. Isn't that unbelievable?

But the company, right now, is very sick, just like on the Ile De France —except for me and another girl, Doris. Poor Charlotte has been desperately sea sick, and all I can do for her is keep a pail close to the bed, and pray not to catch her misery. Even Miss has gone to her stateroom, unable to walk or eat a bite of food.

The sea is especially rough and Doris and I were worried about sleeping in those ailing cabins. Luckily, as we strolled on the nearly empty, rollicking deck—trying to keep dry while seawater sprayed over the railings—we met the ship's captain. He's awfully nice, Captain LeBreton is his name, and he promised to move the two of us to the upper deck. Apparently its off-season, the sea is too rough this time of year, and most of the ritzy berths are empty.

He arranged everything, and now Doris and I are travelling in style. The captain joked that it isn't even second class down there anymore, it's the "sickened class." And he's right.

It's later now, and I wanted to finish this note. The captain invited us to dine with him and the first officer. The few people who were healthy enough appeared for dinner at seven. We all sat together and socialized. The captain rolled out a Victrola and we enjoyed the rest of the evening dancing to scratchy old phonograph records. Remember "Yes, We Have No Bananas"? Those were the kinds of old records he played, *and I enjoyed it enormously.*

I will write more and mail this when we dock in Tunisia.

Dear Mother,

The ship arrived, and the stricken have risen from the depths. In Bizerte, which is in Tunisia, we packed up and left the boat at four in the morning, yawn!

We could have remained aboard and slept later. But we all wanted off that floating infirmary, and the ship wouldn't have arrived in Tunis until 4:00 in the afternoon. Everybody who left with us chipped in, and we hired a bus, very cheap, and it took only an hour to reach Tunis. In fact, nearly the whole troupe opted for that rickety old bus.

It was still dark when we stacked our luggage from the boat to reload on the bus. Out of nowhere, a swarm of men and children wearing robes and rags, descended on our bags, dragging them to the bus for tips.

We girls were surrounded in the chaos, while Earl and the other men fought through the mob, trying to shield us. One man carried my trunk and I handed him a coin, but apparently it wasn't enough, and—this sounds crazy, and I'm all right—but he stormed onto the bus to try to pull me off!

The boys were prepared for him, blocking him in the aisle and throwing him off. Finally everyone safely climbed onboard and the driver apologized again in a high, rapid voice. He wound the doors shut and snaked the bus around the mob, which was hard because it was still dark as midnight.

As it grew lighter the bus followed the most spectacular route along the Mediterranean coastline. My window only opened halfway, and even at dawn the air blew warm in my face. When we arrived in the city it was still early, but we were allowed to check in at the Tunisia Palace Hotel. After such an early start I was happy to be out of the crowds and out of that heat!

Well, that is my tale. Thought you would enjoy the telling.

I'm sending you a money order that should hold you over the holidays. Oh, and I met a nice boy in Brussels. It's nothing serious so don't worry. I will write more soon. Hello to everyone. How is Eileen? Tell her to write.

Love you loads.
Helen the Sailor

Helen,
Your last letter concerned me greatly. Please, please stay out of danger. Never venture out alone. American girls are targets for harems and white slavery. You can't be too cautious. I was so worried, sick with it really, and nearly ordered you home. But you would have had to travel by yourself and that fact stopped me. Who is this boy Helen? I thought we agreed, no boys, and you would concentrate on your dancing!

Your Mother

Dearest Mother,
I have read your letter and I want you to know that Miss has given us that warning already. We never go out alone. Earl Leslie and the other boys keep a close eye on us. There, that should relieve your concern.

North Africa is very strange, but I like it here. Una bought a guidebook and we have, as a group, toured Tunis and Algiers on foot. The buildings are a mix of the past here. The book calls the style "Ottoman-French. I guess that means both Middle Eastern and European.

Every morning we wake up to a public call to prayer. The people are mostly Muslim and the calls are part of their customs. I think it sounds soothing—usually the sound of the caller lulls me back to sleep. Curious, isn't it?

The heat here is dry, and the sun blinding white. We stroll through the narrow streets (in groups) where the sun can't reach us, making for darker, cooler shade. Nameless women veiled from head to toe pull their children along dressed all in white. It's such an exotic world.

Silly as this sounds, I tried to buy you Christmas gifts in the market, but found nothing. You'll have to settle for a telegram, because this is a Muslim country and they don't celebrate Christmas. And, Mother, please have a happy Christmas.

We girls have all decided to do our own gift exchange and sing Christmas carols. We've hung paper chains on a palm tree in the lobby of the Algiers Hotel! The hotel managers gave us permission.

Merry Christmas Mother. I love you and Eileen very much. The young man I mentioned is not serious. His name is Elie, (Jewish, I know) and he has kindly showed us all around tourist sites.

Helen

*

Helen sat cross-legged on her hotel bed, trying to unravel some black thread that had knotted as she mended a zipper.

I've got to lose a few pounds. She shook her head, defeated. *This dress will split wide open the next time I sneeze.*

The company had enjoyed a tranquil Mediterranean return from Africa, and had traveled north, by rail, for a five night engagement in Vienna.

From behind the girl heard a voice softly ask, "Helen? Can I talk to you for a minute?"

Carmen's hushed tone hinted that her friend bore significant news.

"Sure, kid. Let me finish sewing this damn dress back together," Helen answered biting off a final thread. "What's on your mind?" She turned curiously to her favorite fellow dancer.

"Earl wants to marry me, Helen" the dark beauty whispered.

"Oh, Carmen, congratulations! What wonderful news. I had a

feeling he was sweet on you, you temptress," Helen teased, winking her eye.

Carmen tried to smile, but instead, tears abruptly flooded her soft brown eyes and trickled down her cheeks.

"Oh, honey, why the tears? You should be thrilled, at least setting a date, and shopping for a wedding dress!"

"I think Miss found out somehow" Carmen sighed miserably, not hearing her.

"I don't understand. Why do you care if Miss knows?" Helen asked.

"She's been so horrible to both of us," Carmen sniffled.

"Sweet, sweet, Carmen." Helen curved her arm around Carmen's shoulders, "It's just that Miss is so accustomed to being the star. And she's unhappy about getting older. Her looks are fading—that's hard for someone who was once so stunning. She's just jealous, sweetie."

"Yes. I know. Earl knows that too," Carmen wiped her reddened nose on a sodden handkerchief. "But she no longer acknowledges me, and she keeps Earl so busy rehearsing that we hardly have any time together," the girl started crying again. "Earl's started to feel uneasy around Miss, as though she might make a pass at him." Helen mimed gagging.

"So, Helen, we're both going to quit the show, I wanted to tell you first."

"Carmen! Believe me I don't blame you for leaving—I just don't quite know what to say. Where will you go?"

"First to Nice. Earl arranged for us to marry in that little chapel we visited with Elie," her friend, a bit calmer, explained with a tiny smile.

"A German businessman," Carmen continued, "approached Earl while we were in Marseilles, before we sailed for Tunis. His name was something, something Oberst, and he took us to dinner where he made Earl a generous offer to run a string of nearly 40 theaters across Germany. His job will be to book and manage talent for the chain. That decision wasn't too difficult to make."

"I'll miss you, sweetie" Helen replied, her voice slightly strained.

"I'll miss you, too. You've been a good friend," Carmen replied, turning in to hug her pal, as both girls shed fresh tears.

*

After her talk with Carmen, Helen began to sense a distinct shift in the air. The journey that had started with such optimism now seemed lifeless, with uncertainty and friction. Helen soon grasped her time in Europe was rapidly closing, as plainly as summer acquiesced to autumn. Going home seeped into her every thought.

After Earl and Carmen's departure left behind an especially prickly Mistinguett, the tour lost much of its luster. The bond among the rest of the players languished, and it showed in their performances. Helen began exploring ways to find passage to New York.

Dismayed, the girl realized she hadn't saved much money. Her income had been earmarked largely for her mother, and the rest for her traveling expenses. The truth was that Helen couldn't afford a ticket home.

Dissecting her contract, line by line, the homesick girl was unhappy to learn that if she broke her Mistinguett-Lartique contract early, she was financially on her own. If she stayed with the show, that meant working for four more, interminable months in Europe. And *Voila Paris* was slated to leave Vienna shortly, to move on to Budapest, Hungary, then further east to Istanbul, Turkey.

In striking contrast to the previous April, Helen no longer felt any need to travel further into the continent.

Apart from the show losing beloved cast members as well as its esprit de corps, another sinister atmosphere of unrest was drifting across the landscape. At more than one party, someone invariably burned a wine cork and brushed a Hitler mustache above their lip. Blustering loudly in faux German usually netted the comic a laugh or two. But beneath the jokes, Helen felt a menacing uncertainty, and combined with what she saw of regimented Italian fascism, she longed for the sanctuary of home.

Deeply unhappy and in worried frustration, Helen received an unexpected letter from Mr. Evans, her old dance instructor.

> *Helen,*
>
> *Your mother brought you to me when you were just a small child. She had to later confess that she had no money for your lessons because of your father's death. Mrs. Thompson begged me to continue ballet training for you. She said you were a star in the making, and had the discipline and talent to more than make up for her poverty.*
>
> *Because of your mother, I gave you a chance and you have paid her back with scorn and abandonment. You have proven to be nothing but a selfish and worthless girl. How can you continue to stay away like this, hurting your mother, after her sacrifices for you? I am nothing but disgusted with you.*
>
> *E. Evans*

Helen choked through budding tears to finish reading these deeply wounding words. Since she had already begun her plans to go home, Mr. Evans's attack felt particularly wounding and uncalled for.

> *Dear Bert,*
>
> *I received a letter from Mr. Evans. I cannot say his words were unexpected, just that they are undeserved. I have been gone for a long time, but this tour has provided us with a year of income we all sorely needed. I am trying, honestly turning myself inside out, to find a way to New York. Please believe me. I want out of the show and to come home.*
>
> *Helen*

Helen brooded alone in the cluttered dressing room, staring at nothing. Rehearsal had finished, and her friends had gone back to the hotel. Her eyes dropped for the hundredth time to her contract lying among small unguent pots, brushes, and tubes of lipstick.

"What am I missing? What have I overlooked?" Sick at heart,

Helen opened the folded document, and once again began to pour over the fine print.

Using a playbill to underscore each line, Helen's eye caught some language that she thought might lead to her salvation.

> *If injured while performing, the Lartique Agency will assume the cost of the employee's return transportation. The nature and degree of the injury must be verified by a physician.*

"Marseille," she whispered to her image in the mirror. A small ankle sprain Helen had suffered while on stage in France, earlier in the tour, had left Helen hobbling, and out of the show, for a few days. She laughed it off to clumsiness at the time, but now realized that this mishap could mean her passage home.

The girl carefully considered her next move. Grabbing her coat she raced back to the hotel.

"Sir? Sir? Mein Herr?" the girl addressed the desk clerk.

A heavy faced gentleman with strings of graying hair covering his balding head, smiled at the young American girl.

"May I help you miss?" he politely inquired in chopped, nasally English.

"I am looking for a doctor here in Vienna, for a consultation," Helen announced.

"Have you been injured my dear?" The clerk asked concerned.

"No—well, yes, but I need a name if you have one," Helen blushed at her gaffe.

The hotel kept a doctor on call, and while Helen nervously waited, the clerk eventually located the physician. Gesturing for Helen to remain seated, the doctor examined her ankle wordlessly there in the lobby. Gently rotating her foot, he finally shrugged and shook his head.

Head down, she trudged despondently back to her room. The dancer opened the door to see her roommates, Grace and Charlotte happily chatting and painting their nails.

"Looky there, Helen," Charlotte teased, pointing a lacquered nail toward a nightstand. "It's that boy again. He sent more flowers to Lillian."

The girl's head popped up, her eyes reanimated.

Elie Gelaki
C/o Polyphoto
Bruxelles

Elie—Can you find a doctor?—in Paris is best—not to worry—I'm fine—need physician note to go home—
Respond at Vienna address—many thanks—Helen

*

The young businessman wasted no time requesting details, he moved at once. Thrilled to have Helen ask for his aid, Elie placed his pressing business affairs on hold and left Brussels. Traveling the two hours to Paris he promptly began his search for a doctor who could help the girl. Checking with some business contacts he found a general practitioner who, for a fee, would certify anything that Helen required.

Elie cabled his good news to her, and anxiously waited for the girl to steam into Paris. Two days later, medical confirmation in hand, Helen and Elie paid a call at the Lartique Agency, where to her relief the story held up with management. She had hurt her left ankle dancing for Miss in Marseilles. Moreover, Helen had continued to dance on the injury aggravating the damage. The agency readily agreed to book her ticket back to New York.

In a festive mood the couple celebrated with a dinner out. "A toast to New York City," Helen proposed that evening at dinner, raising her fluted glass of champagne.

"And to Bruxelles, the city where we met," Elie rejoined, thrilled to have Helen so vibrant, happy and close, and to have been the man who rescued her.

Glowing at her deliverance and radiant in the candlelight, Helen again offered up her glass. "Let us not forget a toast to beautiful Paris, which I hope to visit again, but not anytime soon."

"To Paris" he repeated softly. Helen, distracted by her own delight, paid no attention to the ache in his tone.

"Please don't say you'll never return" the Belgian whispered in despair, "You're— you're sailing away with my heart."

Helen's face suddenly froze in astonishment. Staggered by his frank admission, she glanced down at her barely touched entree. Her appetite vanished.

*

On April 19, 1933, at the docks in Le Havre, Elie forced a smile on his solemn face as his eyes trailed the beautiful American dancer, loping up the passageway of the S.S. *Ile de France*. Helen, her mind only on her mother and New York, found herself nearly to her cabin when she remembered she hadn't waved goodbye to her friend and benefactor. Guiltily she dashed back to the top deck, only to glimpse Elie disappearing into a taxi slowly rolling away through the cheerful, waving crowd.

FLIRTING
WITH CHEVALIER

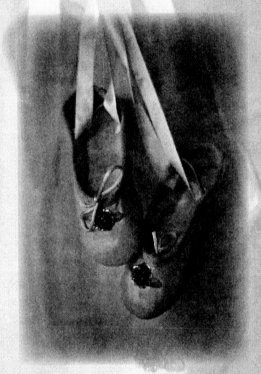

Crossing the Atlantic
1933

Later, unpacking in her berth, Helen considered Elie's passionate dinner admission.

I should have told him sooner that I only wanted his friendship. But would that have changed anything? He appeared almost everywhere we played. And I don't like feeling like this—rude to someone who's been so kind. And he is a nice man. I will write to him and thank him again for his help.

That puzzle set aside for the moment, Helen turned her attention to other, lighter thoughts of New York.

During this Atlantic crossing, some unexpected surprises made it even easier for Helen to leave her regrets behind.

Pulling a metal door ajar at the end of the hall, Helen stepped onto the ship's damp deck. She braced herself against an icy spray, shivering as she pulled up her collar with leather-gloved hands. Her high heels clanked along the metal surface, as she leaned into the wind, stepping toward the ship's ballroom, for a formal dinner and subsequent concert.

Helen puffed her way through the glacial mist, anxious to escape the cold. Picking up her pace, she heard muted shouts from a small betting room along the upper deck. Despite strong gusts of wind, she detected an animated voice on a wireless radio announcing a horse race. Entering a long hallway leading to the ship's stylish social hall, Helen passed the *Ile de France's* windowed recreation center, glancing briefly at travelers playing ping pong on flat green tables and shuffleboard on long narrow lanes.

Stepping into the sparkling ballroom, the dancer presented her card to a uniformed officer, who took her wrap and escorted the American dancer to her table. Helen thanked him as he pushed in her chair, then greeted her dinner companions. The girl gasped as she realized she was staring into the laughing blue eyes of French star, Maurice Chevalier.

"And your name, my dear?" he crooned, amused by his effect.

The flustered girl nervously proclaimed, "Helen Chaddock Thompson."

Chevalier smiled, clearly pleased. Reluctant to move her eyes from the celebrity, she met her other dinner guests that also included the former President of France, Edward Herriot, and French engineer Philippe Bunau-Varilla.

Adding to the introductions, Chevalier leaned over and stage whispered, "That Frenchie, my dear, referring to Bunau-Varilla, sold you Americans the land to build the Panama Canal."

Turning toward President Herriot, Chevalier teased, "Conferring with FDR sir, to save us from Herr Hitler?"

Herriot smiled toward Helen, replying, "We all have our duties, sir."

The chandeliered ballroom, the glittering guests, her witty, brilliant dinner companions, all combined to create a night the dancer could never have imagined.

*

A light knock at her compartment woke the girl the following morning. She groggily unbolted her cabin door and peeked out to see a pleasant faced gentleman that she recognized as the Chief Steward on the Ile de France.

"Good morning Miss Thompson. The Captain has dispatched me to convey his wishes that you consider performing for the passengers this evening."

Helen, still drowsy blinked. "To dance?"

"Yes, if you would be so generous," the young officer politely responded. "We have asked others among our celebrities to join you tonight in a musical review."

"Chevalier, too?"

"Of course, Mademoiselles. We have scheduled Mr. Chevalier to follow your performance."

She smiled through another involuntary yawn. "Please inform the captain that I look forward to appearing, but I will need some time to rehearse with an accompanist, if that is convenient."

"Of course. The salon is available following lunch," the officer bowed, replacing his cap.

That evening, the curtain rose at ten o'clock, in the Grand Salon. Opening first under the spotlight was fellow dancer, French-born Evelyn de la Tour. Helen watched from the left wing, relieved. Unlike Helen, Miss de la Tour tapped a straightforward soft shoe against the jazzy strains of the popular tune, "All of Me."

As the applause quieted, Helen drew in a deep breath and took her spot mid-stage and waited for her cue. The orchestra vocalist began,

"Did you ever see a dream walking?"

Helen shuffled some conventional steps, the buck and wing tap

"Well, I did ..."

Unexpectedly, she curved her torso into a back bend, scissoring her legs gracefully into walkover, sliding effortlessly into the splits.

"Did you ever hear a dream talking? "

Rising agilely, Helen transitioned into a ballet plies

"Well, I did ..."

The girl rose to a full arabesque.

"Did you ever have a dream thrill you with ..."

And an elegant, soaring grand jete`, landing again on-point.

"Will you be mine?"

Both toes on point, the girl stepped into a forward flip.

"Oh, it's so grand and it's too, too divine."

She closed with three rapid spotters, stopping at once, on point, facing the crowd.

The audience responded with audible gasps and applause during her performance. While Helen took her bow, the gathering roared again with approval.

"Thank you, thank you," Helen responded and curtsied.

Chevalier passed her as she exited the stage, nodding his approval with a wink.

The French entertainer then continued the evening, charming the audience with his signature combination of narrative and song, performing "What Would You Do?" from his latest film. Helen watched, captivated, as Chevalier carried the crowd effortlessly from one number to the next. On his last song, the audience rose applauding, as the first notes of the Frenchman's new hit, "Mimi" flowed across the piano.

> *My left shoe's on my right foot—*
> *My right shoe's on my left—*
> *Oh, listen to me Mimi*
> *Of reason I'm bereft...*

For Helen, the night, again, ended too soon when the evening's musical celebration fell silent.

Not a soul moved as President Herriot stepped onto the silent stage. Under a single spotlight the former French president delivered the benediction: "I need not remind this host of the cost of war. We have witnessed the horror of ghastly carnage not so many years ago. Let us all, in this gathering, pray that the power of peace will prevail over the forces of arbitrary power, hate and war."

The girl, leaning against a wall below the stage, whispered, "Amen."

*

On April 22, after three and a half days at sea, the *Ile de France* steamed into New York Harbor. Bags at her side, Helen felt nearly ill with excitement as many in the crowd pointed to the Statue of Liberty, identifiable against the rising New York skyline.

Minutes later, while tugs pushed the ship closer to the dock, the dancer spied her tiny mother straining on her toes to see from the wharf.

Manhattan.

Home.

Helen perched on her tiptoes, as well, watching the crewmen lower the passageway until it reached dockworkers waiting below. Finally, after jostling through the lively flow of passengers, she joyously threw her arms around her smiling mother.

LANDING FIELD #1

Los Angeles
1933

The young pilot sat confidently in his modified Waco, waiting his turn to lift off toward the darkening eastern sky. Whistling tonelessly, set to go, he glanced again at his watch. The race was set to start at 6:30 PM.

The Waco growled restlessly as they delayed, seeded third in line to taxi out. Chum knew the derby rules for takeoff—each entrant had been placed according to engine size and airspeed. So he sat, listening to his insistent motor, as did the four other planes behind him, all anxious to be airborne.

When ground officials finally cleared his Waco, Chum taxied up the runway, gaining speed until he felt his wheels leave the ground. As he rose, the pilot adjusted his instruments, watching his altimeter, airspeed, and angle. Satisfied with his readings, Chum ripped open his Waco to a full throttle—135 miles an hour.

A darkening sky rapidly engulfed the little plane. Testing weather conditions, the pilot watched as night air streamed by, clean and clear, with no crosswind to speak of. Perfect visibility.

Delighted by the view, and with adrenaline pulsing through his body, Chum settled in and pushed on.

As the aircraft sped through the night sky, he began to relax. Below him the Waco's silhouette shadowed ahead, clear over the bluish-white Mojave Desert. The precise relief of the plane, shaped by a full moon, illuminated his corridor eastward. The splendor of the view left him with a deep sense of awe and enormous pleasure. Above the plane, the blending hues of blue revealed blinking stars, leaving Chum feeling lucky indeed to glimpse this world of the night sky.

The pilot carried routing maps on board, and had studied them closely while resting in Glendale. His navigation instruments were simple, but reliable. He monitored his "whiskey compass" for direction and his always dependable, "dead reckoning" techniques. Chum could estimate his position beginning from Glendale—calculating his flight location based on speed and direction. In reality Chum used technology much like that Columbus had available.

Again the pilot tracked the airmail beacons, beaming brightly from the ground, maintaining an eastward course. And despite having plenty of fuel, he was required by derby regulations to land at the first checkpoint, and to confirm his landing with race officials. Chum knew pilots were prohibited from flying beyond the prescribed hours, and stops were verified.

On the ground in Albuquerque, five hours later, after checking in with the ground judge, Chum hopped back into his cockpit. At the same time, a gawky young attendant in grey coveralls leaned from the top of a ladder to fuel the Waco. He thought he heard the boy mumble something about Chum being the second plane to come through that night. Stunned Chum asked him, "What's that, kid?"

"I think you're second, sir," squawked the skinny teenager. As the boy clunked down the ladder, Chum turned over his engine and swiftly taxied down the dark air strip, eyes forward, heart pounding, and lifted off, pushing the Waco to full speed as quickly as the motor allowed.

Damn, I should've asked the ground judge about other racers.
Chum pressed through the night sky. After another long six hours and twenty minutes he spotted a concentration of twinkling lights that could only be Wichita, Kansas. The sun threatened the eastern sky as he skillfully pulled back on the stick, and nosed the Waco onto the landing strip. Before he turned off his engine, judges rushed to confirm his name and plane number, recording his combined time from Albuquerque and Los Angeles.

"Am I the first in?" he called to the judge closest to the plane.

"Affirmative. We're waiting for the other entrants." Chum exhaled deeply. The judge added, "When the next plane lands, the derby rules will spot you the difference in time."

Though he was directed to a bed, he couldn't sleep. As rummy as he felt, the pilot had to wait with the judges for the next racer. Studying the southern sky for a time, they detected a small dot eventually grow into a plane approaching the air field.

Again the judges rushed to the roaring plane, verifying the pilot's name, and recording his time on a clipboard. Returning to the hangar, one of the officials quipped, "You're officially two hours and ten minutes in the lead. Take a nap, will ya' Chumbley, you look like hell."

Chum smiled. Sleep sounded good. His adrenaline was finally burning off and, satisfied of his lead, he looked for a bunk. Cots had been set up in a dark hangar off the field. He gratefully crawled into bed and immediately dropped off.

"Where are they?"

"You say there are two?"

"Quiet down, you jokers. These fellas are tired. Let 'em be."

"Nuts to that captain! My paper wants interviews and pictures."

The rest of the reporters boisterously agreed.

Chum rolled over, momentarily forgetting where he was. The other pilot, a guy named Frank, lay with his arm over his eyes, slowly stretching to the sound of the voices. The two pilots looked at each other, Chum grinned weakly, buttoning his shirt and the two dragged themselves out to meet reporters.

Later, as the ruckus settled, reports arrived that four other pilots had dropped out due to engine trouble or other mechanical foul ups. Some hadn't made it out of Glendale; others ran into trouble heading to Albuquerque. That left only three planes in contention, with the third desperately playing catch-up.

*

Chum departed Wichita at 4:20 PM. Gaining altitude, he looked around his airspace, especially toward the eastern horizon. The pilot yawned, still sleepy, but satisfied he had plenty of daylight to navigate toward Pennsylvania. Listening to his engine hum, he watched a soft, purple-orange evening set in. Clouds started to collect below the Waco, obscuring the ground—his route rapidly grew difficult to navigate.

"If I'm off course I'd better take care of it now," he mumbled. "I can't afford to lose time backtracking later."

Scrutinizing the conditions below him, Chum sighted a small break in the cloud cover. Timing his curve carefully he dipped through the thick bank of mist and spied some ground lights of what must have been an isolated farmhouse. Flying lower, Chum judged a nearby field as fairly level and descended. He set the Waco down executing a bumpy, but acceptable landing.

This plane is honestly the best, he thought, remembering the Harve de Grace Infield.

Turning off the engine, he sat in the silence, as the vibration quieted in his body. Releasing his harness, the worried pilot stumbled across the uneven, muddy ground, and up a dark path. Scraping mud from the bottom of his boots on the porch, Chum stepped up, opened a screen entrance and knocked on a rough wooden door. He heard some bumping, and then a disheveled, astonished farmer, his wife behind him holding a candle, opened the door to the stranger on their porch.

"Sir, Ma'am, I am awfully sorry to wake you," he began politely. "My plane is out on your field, I sure hope you haven't planted anything. I need to get to New York and, well, I'm not sure where I am," Chum explained in a self-effacing tone.

The old man raked him over with an appraising look, then grunted, "You better come in then."

While the wife stirred the fire, put on a pot of coffee, and sliced some cake, the farmer brought out his maps, and smoothed them on his kitchen table, under lamplight.

"Well, you ain't but a tad off, son. This," he pointed to a spot, "is where you are now."

"Oh, that's a relief. Glad you could set me right, sir," he mumbled, his mouth full of angel food cake. Downing the coffee offered, he thanked his accidental hosts and again bumped off the ground into the night sky.

*

A bit anxious by this unscheduled stop, Chum again opened the Waco to full throttle. Visibility hadn't improved, and with time to think, he formed a new plan. Chum decided, *I'll fly out a little over the Atlantic, there's usually a break in the cloud cover there, and then drop down and bank back inland to Long Island.*

But as the morning sky grew lighter, he saw an opening in the thinning clouds. Soon New York City appeared clearly below the plane as visibility improved. By 8:28am, Eastern Time, Montgomery Chumbley lowered his biplane gently, bouncing once down runway number two, Roosevelt Field, his final destination.

The young pilot was weary, but gratified by his hotly contested success. Taxiing his plane toward the hangar, Chum watched race officials rush en mass to greet him on the landing strip.

Some reception, he thought, as he reached over to turn off his engine. But these men were all waving their arms so frantically that he thought that maybe there was an emergency, and his plane might be needed.

"Chumbley! Chumbley," he could hear from his now open window.

"You've landed on the wrong airstrip!"

"You need to move over to runway number one. My God, man, don't shut off the engine or you're disqualified!"

Without any conscious thought, or hesitation, Chum turned the plane toward the correct landing strip and taxied over as fast as he safely could. When he, at last, shut down the Waco, only two minutes were added to his airtime of 24 hours and 26 minutes, a new transcontinental night flying record.

Finally leaning against his plane, stretching his legs, a tired but gratified Chum heard a loudspeaker blare, "The winner of the 2000 mile Darkness Derby is Roosevelt Field's own, Monty Chumbley!"

Resting in the back of Howard Ailor's office—his office, Chum awaited the other two competitors. His bunkmate from Wichita landed four hours later, clocking in at thirty hours and sixteen minutes. In third place and the only other flight to arrive, was the California pilot who made up time skipping sleep, coming in at thirty hours and forty-one minutes. Later, appearing before cameras and reporters, Chum and his weary associates were all smiles.

"So who's the best flyer here?" shouted a reporter from the Long Island Telegram.

The three looked at each other, grinning awkwardly.

"I guess it's Chumbley," responded the second place finisher. The boys from the Waco hangar liked that, and turned loose a torrent of hoots and applause.

At the Capitol Theatre, the following night, the derby prizes were awarded before a live audience. Screening a first run film, "Night Flight" starring Helen Hayes, John and Lionel Barrymore, Clark Gable, and Myrna Loy, Chum accepted his accolades from lead actress, Miss Hayes.

"We, in the movies pretend to achieve dramatic accomplishments," she said. "But our real champions stand on this stage tonight."

Amidst the resounding applause, Miss Hayes then handed Chum an enormous silver trophy, complete with a tiny silver airplane on top sporting a little propeller that twirled. He also received a check for $1500—more money than he had ever seen. In the days after the race, Chum repaid Ross for refitting his plane, and paid his mother back for his plane's down payment. Free and clear for the first time since the Navy, his earnings now belonged to him.

Newspapers in Albuquerque, Wichita, and New York all published stories on the Darkness Derby. Picking up the *Times*, Chum read the bi-line, "Swooping his Waco Cabin Biplane into Roosevelt Field." The piece identified him as a "socialite pilot." Further into the article the reporter added that Chum was a "well known New York pilot of photographic planes…"

That should help business, the pilot noted, pleased.

A couple weeks after the race Ailor picked up an insistent phone.

"Mont Chumbley, please," a male voice demanded.

"He's out flying," Ailor replied.

"I'm Preston Martin, Kendall Oil Company. Tell that boy we want him to advertise our product," Martin insisted. And true to Martin's word, before long Chum's picture appeared in aviation journals and commercial magazines. Depicted in an oval photograph, trophy in hand, the pilot smiled beside a written testimonial on the benefits of Kendall Oil, and how it certainly had helped him win the race. Waco soon followed up, hiring him to appear in a company advertisement. Posed alongside an elegant brunette, Chum sat in the backseat of a Waco Cabin Plane, as if the couple was snuggling into a sedan with a chauffeur at the wheel.

It tickled Chum to do the shoot, and he liked the money too. And as he told Ailor, "This Company does make a good product. You should've seen some of the harebrained landings the plane and I have both survived!"

Later, the Navy recognized the young reservist, honoring him with a promotion to Ensign. Frances, the married object of his desire, teased him asking, "Well, Navy, what are you going to do with all that money and fame?"

He grinned at this unobtainable dark beauty and flirted back, "It's in the bank, baby," and winked.

*

"What the hell do I do with all this mail, Howard?" Chum stared, overwhelmed at the small mountain of envelopes overflowing from his desk.

Ailor laughed, "You're a celebrity now, pal; fame bears a heavy crown."

"These letters come from Tennessee, Hollywood, Omaha, Missouri—and folks want all sorts of things. My autograph. To find out if I'm related to their family. Will I join their aviation clubs, speak at their conventions, asking if I know Wiley Post or Charles Lindbergh. I don't know where to begin!"

"Look kid," his friend advised, "You're only 24 years old. Don't worry about pleasing all these people. Answer a couple letters, politely decline the membership offers, and thank everybody for their good wishes."

Then Howard's expression softened. "You did real well, Chum. I imagine your folks must be awfully proud of you."

*

His minor fame did improve his air business. Customers tracked him down at the field for all kinds of jobs. First, and always foremost, Chum made himself available to Ailor— still demonstrating new Wacos and flying Howard's potential customers on short flights.

"I'm looking for a Mont Chumbley, and the gentleman in the office sent me out here," a well-dressed New Yorker explained, entering the Waco hangar.

"I'm Chumbley" Chum replied, wiping grease off his hands.

"Look, I'm interested in purchasing an airplane, but I need a little help," the man explained.

"Certainly. What can I do?" Chum asked.

"Teach me how to fly!" Then the fellow grinned.

"Name's Hayward, Leland Hayward," he stuck out his right hand. "I work on Broadway. I'm an agent. And I sure want to learn to fly airplanes."

"Happy to know you Mr. Hayward," Chum shook his hand. "When would you want to begin?"

In the weeks following Hayward's introduction, and after a couple of sessions in the cockpit, Hayward asked, "Would you mind if I brought my girlfriend to fly with us next time? She's just back from California."

"Fine by me Mr. Hayward. We'll buzz Manhattan—you can put it down in Central Park." Chum winked.

"You're a funny guy, Chum," Hayward replied.

At his next lesson, Hayward indeed showed up with his girlfriend. And Chum couldn't help noticing everyone turned their heads as she walked across the field, arm-in-arm with his student-pilot.

As the couple approached, his client gestured, "This is Mont Chumbley."

"Hey," Mont smiled, thinking the girl striking.

"And Chum, this is my friend, Kate."

After Chum landed back on the field and the couple drove off, Frances burst into the hangar, finding Chum bent over inside his plane clearing out the cabin.

"Chum, how did you meet her?" Frances asked.

"Who?" the pilot looked perplexed.

"Katherine Hepburn, Chum! For crying out loud, she's a movie star!"

After another lesson, Frances informed her friend that one of the students he was instructing in navigation was cosmetic giant, Jacqueline Cochrane. "Frances, my dear, I don't care if they're famous. I just don't want them to crash my airplane.

*

"Ailor's looking for you" a mechanic hollered into the hangar.

"Me, Woody?" Chum called back.

"Yeah. He's on the phone in his office."

Rain had just started spotting the gravel while the pilot walked over to the Waco Office.

"What do you say, Howard?" Chum warmly greeted his friend.

"People, Chum. So damn difficult!" He sighed, "I have a customer down in Florida—West Palm Beach, who's interested in a Cabin monoplane. He apparently needs it to fly friends to Los Angeles, all a big rush. He'll buy, if the plane is there by morning. You get first crack at the delivery if you want it."

"Geez. Well, Howard, ah, you know, I think I'd like to take that flight," Chum wavered and slowly decided. "Night is a great time to fly—very peaceful. And things here are pretty quiet. Yeah, you got yourself a pilot."

Refueling in Raleigh and again in Savannah, the young man managed to land the new model at the West Palm airstrip on time, taxiing to the numbered hangar, about 7:30 AM the next morning. "Who are you?" asked the tall, thin, dark-haired client. "Where'd that plane come from? You couldn't be here all the way from New York?!"

Too groggy to argue Chum replied, "Howard Ailor sent me down with your plane. Flew here overnight."

"Not possible" the client insisted. "That's not the plane I ordered. This one has to be used."

"Sir, I was asked to fly this Waco down from Roosevelt Field. It's new, not used, and it's yours."

"I'm calling my head mechanic over—he'll know if it's new or not," the tall man challenged. "What's your name young man?"

"Chumbley, sir. Mont Chumbley."

"You must be one hell of a pilot, Chumbley, if you're not trying to put one over on me. I've never known any flyer that could have make that trip from New York. My name's Hughes. Howard Hughes, but I guess you knew that. I just don't believe you got here overnight. What time did you leave last night?"

"About ten, sir. Only stopped to refuel and eat. Can I get a lift to the train station? I need to get back to New York," the sleepy pilot requested.

As though he wasn't listening Hughes replied, "I don't believe this. Ailor is pulling something here. It's impossible that you flew here that fast."

"Sir—Mr. Hughes, I don't mean to be rude, but I have a business to run at Roosevelt Field. I need to get home. I'm not making any money here. Your issue is with Mr. Ailor. I delivered the plane, and now I need a lift to the train station."

Hughes began walking toward his hangar as if Chum hadn't spoken. He heard Hughes shout, "Get Rusty out here to look this Waco over, and get Ailor on the phone in New York."

For the next two days Hughes and Ailor wrangled back and forth, via telephone, between Florida and New York. Chum impatiently hung around the hangar waiting for some kind of resolution.

"This engine's used. I won't buy the plane," Hughes finally informed the young pilot. "But Chumbley, you sure know your way around a propeller. I'm going to keep you instead."

PHOTO GALLERY

Martha Jane (Surratt) Chumbley, 1906

Mont Chumbley and Brazilian official, 1934

Mont Chumbley, Aero Magazine, winner of 1933 Darkness Derby

Mont Chumbley with actress Helen Hayes presenting the trophy, 1933

Mont Chumbley in Rio de Janeiro, 1936

"The Ninety Nines," 1933
Frances Marsalis, center, Amelia Earhart, left

Helen Thompson, front, with Bela Lugosi, left
"Women of All Nations," 1930

Helen Thompson, fifth left, Maurice Chevalier, second left
On the Ile De France, 1934

Helen Thompson, center, with Don Dean conducting, right
The Don Dean Orchestra, Buenos Aires, 1936

Helen Thompson and Grant Garrett
On the road, 1931-32

Helen Thompson with Harry Jans and Harold Whalen
London Palladium, 1934

Helen and Chum
Copacabana Beach, 1936

Helen Thompson and Montgomery Chumbley
New York, 1936

Bertha (Locke) Thompson
New York, 1934

STANDSTILL
IN NEW YORK

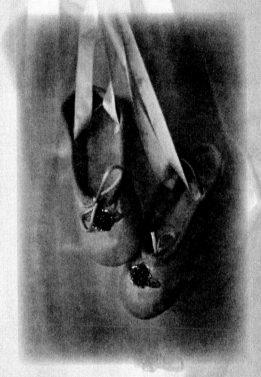

London
1934

New York felt a bit like purgatory after the excitement of Europe and Helen's incredible voyage home. To the newly returned dancer, the city looked dreary. There were no new productions worth auditioning for, and the theatre district felt dreary and lifeless, starving from a severe shortage of investors.

Scouring trade papers at the Whitby Hotel, Helen noticed even fewer productions off-Broadway, or in Manhattan dinner clubs.

"Hey Bert," she sarcastically reported, "There's a revival of Chekov's 'The Cherry Orchard,' oh, and Erskine Caldwell's 'Tobacco Road.' How jolly. Bet they'll be rolling in the aisles at those theaters."

"But look there, sweetheart, some Gilbert and Sullivan revivals, too—'HMS Pinafore,' 'The Mikado,' and 'The Pirates of Penzance.' It isn't all glum," her mother pointed out in an inflated cheery voice, peeking over her shoulder.

Helen shot Bertha a sour expression, "*Billboard* and *Variety,* gone through them both," Helen complained, "There are fewer vaudeville auditions available than before I left. You know, Mother, everywhere we played in Europe the dismal job situation in New York came up in conversation."

Bertha frowned; a worried look appeared in her eyes.

That afternoon, collecting the mail down in the lobby, Helen grumbled, *boy oh boy. Highlight of my day.*

However, finding a letter from Eileen in the stack brightened her spirits. Skipping back up the stairs a little lighter, the girl tore the envelope open, finding a letter and a check inside.

"Letter from Eileen," Helen sang. "I guess we'll eat again tomorrow."

Helen handed her mother the money order, while she focused on the letter. "She says she's tried, but there's no place for me in her show." Helen frowned.

"Good," Bertha muttered. "I just got you home."

Helen shot her another sassy look.

"I need to find something, anything!" She raised her hands in the air dramatically, and slapped her arms down by her side. "And this waiting is miserable."

A mild, comfortable June transitioned into a sweltering July, and July into a suffocating August. Seated near a whirling fan, listening to the blades rhythmic scratch, Helen smoked cigarettes, read the trade papers, and listened to the radio. Bertha pretended to stay busy in the boxed-sized kitchenette, avoiding her daughter's petulant mood.

"Two nights at the Orpheum, in Manhattan, one performance at the RKO Theatre in Brooklyn, and a weekend out in Jersey City. I guess I can retire," Helen griped.

Bertha grimaced but said nothing.

The girl's misery soured to near despondency with the unexpected arrival of an uninvited visitor.

*

"All you have to do, my dear, is slightly adjust your pose after each click," Elie smiled, nonchalantly smoothing her curls. Helen merely nodded.

Elie had planned this crossing of the Atlantic "to enlarge his business interests in New York City" as he explained to Helen. She smiled automatically, nodding in understanding but nowhere close to convinced. Since Elie's abrupt arrival, the time he had devoted to his company seemed a fraction of the time he spent with her at the Whitby.

"Now, Mother, please sit on the stool and shift as Helen has," Elie politely instructed, guiding Bertha by her elbow. "Before Helen and I have married, I hope to host Sister Eileen for a sitting as well."

Bertha's alarmed eyes darted to her daughter, who rolled hers in reply. Neither woman responded—Elie smiled, reading their silence as approval.

"Remember my dear girls, I will collect you both at seven this evening. We shall dine at an eatery of your choosing," Elie reminded them at the studio door. He then leaned in, and aiming for Helen's mouth, kissed her chin instead as she twitched her head.

She saved his dignity, joking, "You caught me off-guard," and smiled at him.

Leaving Broad Street, mother and daughter strode silently for a few blocks. Suddenly Helen turned to her mother in exasperation exclaimed, "Sometimes when I feel stuck, like right now, marrying Elie seems like my only alternative! He certainly loves me enough, and is financially stable!"

Lost in their thoughts, the two women again resumed their pace. Walking another block in silence, Bertha finally spoke, "He behaves as a man should, Helen. I will give him credit for that. But, you still have a career and fame ahead of you. I won't permit you to give that up for any man."

*

"When do I finally meet the debonair European?" Eileen, home for Christmas, teased.

"If he had his way it would be tomorrow at our wedding. Thank goodness he sailed back," Helen sighed, thoroughly exhausted with the subject of Elie.

"That bad?" Eileen, sympathetically asked.

"Worse," Helen frowned. "But, on the brighter side, the Grant situation seems to have died down. He's been divorced for months now, and hasn't made any mad dashes to New York."

"You hurt by Grant's silence?" Eileen asked.

"No, surprisingly not." Helen confessed. "Actually, I'm relieved—with Elie so relentless, one suitor is plenty. Besides, Bert hasn't complained about Grant in months. Let's not bring his name up; it sets her off," she frowned.

"Deal, Sis. Consider my silence your Christmas present," Eileen squeezed her hand.

After the holidays Helen returned to her same tired routine, scouring through the entertainment section of *Variety*, perusing the "Dancers Needed" column. Peering over her coffee cup, a fresh ad caught her practiced eye. "Needed: female comic-dancer. Some singing required."

Helen carefully penciled the contact number into her address book. She picked up the receiver from the heavy black telephone base, and began to dial.

*

"Mother—Bert! I have an audition in the morning! Do you hear me? Where are you? I have an audition," the girl called.

"Goodness, Helen" her mother cried out. "Can't I make my bed without your permission? Now what's all this fuss about?"

"I have an audition tomorrow at ten! It's with a vaudeville team, Harry Jans and Harold Whalen. Have you heard of that act? I haven't." she chirped happily. "I'm meeting them at a dance studio off Times Square. Do you want to come along?"

Bertha smiled, pleased to finally hear good news. "I'll be there with bells on!"

*

Jans and Whalen were known in New York and Hollywood as "Two Good Boys Gone Wrong." They had enjoyed minor fame on vaudeville stages and in west coast comedy films. By the spring of 1934, the team had successfully negotiated a new contract to sail to England and play the legendary London Palladium. The partners had agreed that they needed a third partner, and decided on an ingénue to glamourize their act a bit.

Helen, toting her mother along, found the address of a small studio off 45th, not too far from their apartment. Helen pulled the heavy glass door open, and lodged her foot on the base, allowing Bertha to pass through first. She could hear voices from down a dark hallway.

"What did Hitler say when he got caught in the rain?"

"I don't know, Jans. What did Hitler say when he got caught in the rain?"

"Mein Damph!"

"I don't know, Whalen. That kind of joke can come off flat. Do you know what I'm saying?"

"What about: what did Hitler say in his weather report?" Helen quietly offered.

A friendly dark-haired man with a confident smile approached her. "What did Hitler say in his weather report?"

Helen smiled shyly, "Reign today, heil tomorrow."

The man laughed. "Good one, I like it better. Glad you could make it. I'm Harry Jans, and that handsome specimen is my partner, Harold Whalen."

The partner smiled kindly, and nodded.

"I'm Helen, Helen Thompson and this is my mother and manager, Bertha Thompson."

"Mrs. Thompson," Jans acknowledged. Turning back to Helen he chirped, "You're right on time, young lady. What do you have for us today?"

"Here's my sheet music," Helen said. Whalen took the piece to the piano.

"I like this song," Harold Whalen commented.

"Me, too" Helen replied.

Whalen tinkled out a jazzy introduction to Gershwin's "I Got Rhythm." The girl began with a light soft shoe, progressed to flips, and finished with poised ballet leaps. When the music ended, Jans looked at her with an awed expression, and then turned to Whalen with his mouth slightly open.

"Thanks Helen, very well done," he said. "We have a few more appointments today and—is this phone number the best way to contact you?"

"Yes," Bertha interrupted while Helen stood puffing, her hand pressing her right side. As mother and daughter left the studio, Helen turned to her mother gasping, "I'm so out of shape. I hope they didn't notice how breathless I became."

"Sweetheart, they were captivated" Bertha squeezed the girl's arm.

Entering the Whitby lobby, Helen offered, "I'll get the mail, Mother. You go on ahead."

Bertha shuffled across the small foyer and up the staircase. The dancer, still breathing a bit hard, inserted her key into the lock of the small, ornate brass mailbox, finding the slot packed full of envelopes. Her expression grew apprehensive, as she removed an onionskin, airmail envelope, embossed with numerous European blue stamps.

> *My Dearest Helen,*
> *Greetings to you and your wonderful mother and your sister, whom I hope to soon meet. I am pleased to inform you that I shall cross the Atlantic again to tend to my New York interests. Please make time in your busy schedule to spend with me as you are the delight in my world.*
> *Sincerely With Love, E*

ONLY YOU

Crossing the Atlantic
1934

The girl stood in the lobby brushing the stationary absently across her left hand fingers. "He's coming here and I hope to be going there. How typical for this situation. We've never quite connected in so many ways."

Wearily Helen hiked up to the apartment on the third floor, pushing the door closed with her hip, listening for the latch.

"Mother," she called out. "Elie's coming back."

From the narrow hall she heard her mother sigh.

*

"Try this black dress. It has a veil and a lace black umbrella." Whalen quietly fussed and adjusted Helen's costume.

"All right," she stood still while her new partner coiled the gown over her head.

"How does this look?" Helen stepped back, while Whalen appraised her.

"Perfect, Helen. I thought we'd have to alter the waist, but you've trimmed down."

"I should hope so," the dancer laughed, "I think Jans planned an exercise schedule and just called it rehearsal."

It was a mild May afternoon in 1934 when Jans and Whalen, with their new partner Helen Thompson, met on the docks to set sail on the *S.S. Aquitania.*

*

"Helen," Elie grasped her upper arms. "I'm not sorry I came to New York even to see you for such a brief time. I—I want you more than any other ambition in my life." Elie's face twisted with pain. "And my dearest girl, I don't believe I shall ever again lay eyes on you after this ship sails today."

"Elie please, it's only a four-week engagement." The girl awkwardly soothed him.

"My heart tells me you will never marry me." His eyes closed. "And for me there is no one else, only you."

Helen stared at his tie tack, a lustrous pearl on a grey tie.

"I will never change my heart or my mind. It's only you for the rest of my days," Elie lamented.

"Cheer up. I'll see you soon." Helen forced a smile, lightly pecked the Belgian on the cheek, and rushed up the busy gangway, escaping. When she joined the crowd at the top deck railing she spied Elie, and he hadn't moved an inch. He caught her eye, and gazed back intensely, unresponsive to her friendly wave. Ashamed, she stepped away from the guardrail and disappeared into the animated crowd. Her remorse pressed on her heavier than her steamer trunk.

"What did you say to that poor guy? Is he your boyfriend, Helen?" Jans abruptly asked, stopping her as she pressed through passengers.

"Oh, Harry, he'd like to think so. I feel so bad. His name's Elie and he is crazy about me."

"Not your cup of tea, then."

"I honestly don't know. The way he dotes on me leaves me bewildered. Sometimes I think I should marry him; other times I want to run the other way."

Jans gently took both of Helen's hands in his. "Honey, if you loved that boy, you wouldn't have boarded this ship. You wouldn't have auditioned for the act. Your heart would be floating, overflowing with joy."

The dancer looked at her new partner and smiled at his kind

words, though she felt more like weeping.

Jans read her thoughts. "Helen, when you fall in love—and you will, nothing will feel the same. Your life will shift unexpectedly off course, and you will follow it gladly."

"Thanks Harry," Helen sniffled, tears now rolling down her cheeks.

"Now, now. None of that," Jans kindly scolded. "Geez, kid, you needed a trip!"

*

Dearest Bert,

We enjoyed a safe, but drenching voyage to Plymouth. I had to find Jans and Harold Whalen on the deck so we could ride the train into London together. It was a black umbrella convention!

I have to admit I panicked a little trying to find the boys under every "bumbershoot"—nearly slipped on the wet top deck in my heels, but finally caught sight of Whalen waving his hat—he saw me first. It's funny how much Harry Jans and Harold Whalen look alike, but they couldn't be more different. Jans is all business and confidence while Whalen is so fragile. It's like one word might break him in two. He's very sweet.

When I caught up with them Jans announced "Come hither my good lady, our chariot awaits."

It made me laugh while Whalen just grinned. Glad we were having a laugh, because the footrace to the train risked bodily injury. I took hold of both their sleeves so we could stay together and we splashed quickly to the rail platform.

Then wouldn't you know it, the compartments were full and so humid. Sweat dripped down every window as we searched for an empty berth. Finally, in the last carriage, Jans spotted an empty compartment. It seated four, but we took up all the space. Whalen surprised me by making a fourth rider out of our luggage. It was hilarious, and the conductor didn't even care, he didn't even look up. Even with the train so crowded. Mother, they are such nice gentlemen. I thanked them for hiring me. Jans told me they were the lucky ones. Sweet isn't it.

As you can see by this stationary we are booked at The Cumberland Hotel. It is so grand, so modern. I have my own sink! We still navigate down the hall for the lavatory, but the sink makes such a difference. I can wash my hair and my undergarments in private. Hip Hip Hooray!

More Later,
Helen

Dear Dorothy,

I am sorry to write to you in a crisis, but I have dreadful news. Please keep what I'm about to tell you a secret—not a word to my Mother or my sister, please. We've been fired! I know—it's horrible. I don't know what we'll do. Jans says he can fix it, but I'm not so sure. I may have to come home early. I am writing to you because I can't say a thing to my Mother— you know how she gets. But I may need a little money to get home. I do promise to pay you back when I get on my feet.

We made our first trip to the Palladium, they lettered my name on the billboard "Helen Thompson, Our Saucy Soubrette" whatever that means. I thought it was cute. Anyhow, we entered the theatre through the back entrance and met a lot of the cast. Such nice people, too. They told us that "The Crazy Show," that's what they call it, has been coming back to the Palladium for years. This group of comedians is known, together, as the "Crazy Gang" and made us feel very welcome. They explained that the same crowds return each season to see their old friends in the show.

We felt pretty excited opening night when Jans and Whalen took the stage after the all-cast extravaganza and began their routine. Harry Jans told the one about the soldier who had survived mustard gas and pepper spray becoming a seasoned veteran. No on laughed. The audience hated them. No one booed, and they clapped a little when Jans played and sang, "Miss Porkington Would Like Creampuffs." Remember that silly song? Other than that polite response, not a snicker sounded in the whole house.

Then I went on stage and performed a widow comedy monologue; black gown, the whole bit, and I bombed too. With all those spotlights trained on me, if it hadn't been for the coughing and murmuring I would have thought the theater empty. It was horrible— nauseating— I couldn't believe how miserably we failed. WE LAID AN EGG!

After the show some of the regulars took us out for drinks. I wanted to run back to the hotel and hide. They led us to a nice pub, but I felt so shook up I could hardly light my cigarette. They explained that English audiences often don't understand American humor. In particular, my widow act seemed more offensive than funny.

"Too many widows after the Great War," one comedian named Eddie Gray told me. "Not funny to families with loved ones who died in the trenches."

That never crossed my mind, Dot. It's been almost 15 years, for goodness' sake. So we were ready to make the changes the boys in the cast suggested. No prohibition jokes, no dead jokes, more songs, and lighter skits. When we arrived for rehearsal the next morning letters were pinned to the dressing room doors that we were to clean our things out—that the management would no longer honor our contract. By the way, the Times critics gave us a lambasting, too. I got to feel mortified all over again.

So, dear Dorothy, that is how the situation stands. Whalen won't come out of his room. Jans is ready to murder the guy in the front office, and I may drag out my trunk and mail myself home. Just let me know if you can cover my passage. But, don't do anything yet.

Thanks oodles and oodles and mum's the word.

Helen

My Dear Friend Dorothy,

Salvation! We have been kept on the bill, at least for a couple of small bits. So thanks for agreeing to help me home, but Jans did take care of things. I swear, Dot, Harry Jans could coax the English rain back into the gray English clouds. It all happened so quickly, but this is how events turned. We were shocked, and then worried, as I'm sure you could tell. Then Jans remembered that our contract explicitly stated we were to make $1000 dollars a week regardless of circumstances. He marched into the manager's office and wouldn't leave until he received a check for $4000 dollars, or our reinstatement to the show. The manager balked and then Jans reiterated that the contract was clear. My partner gets a little fierce when he's riled and I think he scared the fellow. The manager said he'd discuss it with his investors.

But that's not the best part. The whole cast refused to go on until we were back on the billing! Their leader, Teddy Knox, told the manager that one night wasn't fair, and that until we went on again, they would wait. All of them! Bless their hearts! Guess they are crazy. Later, I caught up with Teddy Knox in the green room and told him how grateful I was. I guess I just hugged him and cried.

So all is well, and Bertha still calm. I will tell her, but will word my letter so that she doesn't blow her stack. Thanks again, Dot. You are such a swell friend!

Helen

Dear Bert,

We have had quite a hectic week. We opened on Thursday night and were fired Friday morning. Can you believe that? But don't panic, we're back on the bill now. It was all a misunderstanding; apparently people in England and people in the States laugh at different things, so we changed our act a bit. Should be all right now. Jans and Whalen are keeping a close eye on me so don't worry. I will send a money order in my next letter and hopefully more news. Don't worry Mother. Things here are fine. Love to Eileen.

Love,
Wellen

Helen,
   I don't understand how you could take firing lightly. If there are any further problems you catch the first ship home. You tell Harry Jans that I mean it. Now take care, and make sure you keep me informed of any other issues.
                    Mother

Dear Mother,
   I hope that you aren't too cross with me. We won't be gone long, and I will be home very soon. The three of us are back in the lineup. Jans and Whalen play toreadors in the opening number, and I am in a black and white feather costume complete with white boots. The outfits are very snazzy. We sing the show's theme song, "Come Round London with Me," then "God Save the King." We had to rehearse them both, and the audience stands up and sings along when "God Save the King" begins. Can you believe it?
   Jans and I finally are doing our own skit. I wear my tap shoes, a short flared skirt with suspenders and a huge pink bow in my hair. On cue I timidly step to center stage (everyone can hear each tap). Under the spotlight Jans, says "Did you come out to sing a song for the nice people?"
   I point to my throat and croak out "l-a-r-y-n-g-i-t-i-s."
   Jans answers, "Oh, that's a shame we all were looking forward to your number."
   I lean over and whisper into Jans' ear. Jans then says loudly "You want to whisper the words to me, and I sing the song?

Yes, yes, a grand idea! I would love to!" He announces "This song is called "Where on Earth could all the Fairies Be?"

I whisper in his ear, he sings a line, next whisper, he sings, and then Jans finishes, arms opened wide belting the out the refrain, "Where on Earth could all the Fairies Be?"

A spotlight quickly hits Jimmy Naughton, (he's a Brit) planted up in the balcony who calls out in an effeminate voice, "Oh, my, where aren't they?" The lights cut to black and the crowd roars with laughter. Cute, huh?

Did you receive the money I mailed?

It won't be long now,
Little Sister

Dearest Helen,

Hope that you are staying safe and minding your manners. The show sounds quite good. Your sister is now working in Indianapolis in a new production. I'm here by myself. Hope you get home soon. I didn't get out of bed today. No one to get out of bed for. Your envelope arrived safely to the apartment.

Your Mother

Dearest Bert,

I am so happy to hear that Eileen is working. That has to be a relief, doesn't it? I'll be home before you know it. Hang on. The boys and I have been sightseeing. We toured mostly on foot using Whalen's walking map. We saw Buckingham Palace—it's so regal, so beautiful, so big!

Jans and Whalen horsed around in front of the Beefeaters guarding the palace. How could two comedians resist? Jans danced a wild Charleston nearly in a guard's front pocket, but the sentry did not so much as blink. We later ambled through Kew Gardens alive with color though it's been unusually cool and rainy.

Whalen led the way to Big Ben, but we were disappointed when we got there. The clock tower is covered by layers of scaffolding because it's under renovation and difficult to see. Whalen shocked us when he stepped past the pedestrian barricades to get a better look. Though nervous, we followed him and I'm glad we did. The tower is huge!

It's rained so much that we went shopping at Harrods and bought umbrellas for sightseeing. And yes, we stopped at London Bridge where we took a lot of snapshots that I guess you have already seen since they were in this envelope.

As you can tell mother it's not 'falling down' like they used to sing. I've enclosed a money order for $75.00.

Love, Helen

Helen,

Hearing of your tour makes me wonder when you have had time to perform. Keep your attention on your career. You are there for experience and exposure. I saw Mr. Evans today and showed him your letter. He is disappointed too. Keep your mind on your work.

Mother

Dearest Mother,

I have the most wonderful news. Charlotte and Grace are working here in London, too! I had been reading the theater guide in The Times *and the girls are opening at the Savoy Theatre. We walked down there to see if they were around— and by the way, the Savoy looks just like* The New York Times *Building. We went backstage and they were there. They were as tickled to see me as I was to see them. They are such swell friends.*

Jans and Whalen laughed at us as I introduced everybody (we jumped around hugging and squealing). Jans promised we would come to their opening night and we did. I think Jans just wanted to scout out the competition. The show wasn't so hot. Whalen tried to say nice things, like "lovely costumes" and "enjoyed that American quartet."

I told him I didn't think it too great, either. But this one group could really sing, Mother. Jans found their name on the bill, they were The Mills Brothers. Best act I've seen so far in London, except us, ha. They sang some songs we have heard on the radio in New York, "Sweet Sue", "Tiger Rag", "Chinatown, My Chinatown," remember? Try to stay happy till I get there. Don't let Mr. Evans tell you any different. Have you heard from Eileen or Elie Gelaki?

Love,
Number Two Daughter

Dear Helen,

Eileen won't be home for weeks; her show is playing on the road. She said she would look again for a place for you in the production when you get back. I hope you can find work in New York—you've been gone long enough, for heaven's sake. I think Elie returned to London. He never came by to see me again. I don't know what became of him. Carrie Whalen came by and she wants Harold home as much as I want you here.

Mother

AMERICAN FRIENDS

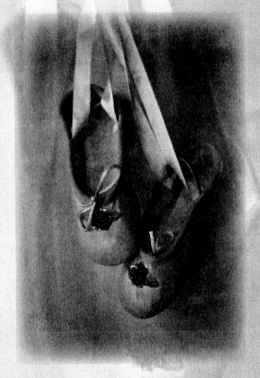

London
1934

"Where do you and Charlotte get your hair washed and set?" Helen wondered, reclining across her little bed. Her four friends, Harold, Harry, Grace and Charlotte were intently studying cards, absorbed in a rubber of bridge. The little group sipped English tea, while rain splattered against the window. Grace lay down her cards, removed her cigarette from her lips and replied, "We do each other's. We can't afford a salon on what the Savoy pays us."

Grace picked up her hand, extracted a card, slapping down a trump. Helen laughed.

"You women going to style hair or play cards?" Jans sourly complained.

Later, after Grace and Charlotte had collected their winnings and said goodnight, Harry Jans exited too. Whalen loitered behind seeming anxious to talk to Helen.

"I do hair." He mumbled, looking at the floor. "I can wash and set. Do my mother's all the time."

Helen paused, concerned. *What could he know about women's hair?* But dear Whalen gave her such an earnest, trusting look that she nodded toward the miniscule powder room, "Think there's enough space for the two of us to wedge in there?" She teased. Whalen laughed.

The following afternoon Harold Whalen pushed cheerfully through her door carrying a towel, a comb, and a bottle of chardonnay. With a festive flair, he uncorked the wine. They drank a toast, and then Helen dunked her head in the sink, while Whalen began singing a falsetto aria from *The Barber of Seville*. In playful spirits, Whalen lathered her up and helped her rinse under the inadequate little faucet. While she towel-dried her hair he quietly offered, "I'd be happy to set the back in pin curls while you set the front."

Again surprised by his offer, she thought a moment, and then decided that Whalen probably did know about styling.

"Sure, my bobby pins are in the pink bag on my bed. I'll grab a chair."

As Whalen hummed and worked he casually remarked, "Helen, I mean no offense, but it looks like your roots could use some attention. I'll pop by the chemist tomorrow and pick up some peroxide. We'll take care of it after rehearsal."

"Oh," she said, turning pink. "Thank you."

*

"Helen? Helen, can you come out here?" Jans shouted from his dressing room door.

"Coming Harry" she called back from the girl's quarters, tying the strings of her robe. Hurrying into the passageway she found Jans in the middle of the hall. He spoke in a low voice declaring, "My money is missing. I think I've been robbed."

"Robbed? How much did you leave in your room?"

"Five pounds and it's gone. Some schmuck must have come in while we were performing."

Word of this dressing room heist spread like lightning back stage, with most in the company sure of the guilty party. Players approached Jans, one by one, and told him that they had been hit the same way over the last few weeks—all while on-stage. Popular opinion pointed to an English vaudevillian named Eric the Midget, Comedian Extraordinaire.

Baffling to all the victims was that no one could prove it; he was never sighted backstage alone. Nor did Jans or the other victims recover any of their losses. In the dim light, among the ropes, sand bags, props, and rushing stagehands, all eyes monitored Eric's location much more closely.

Though truly sorry that Harry Jans had been wronged, the

pint-sized accused perpetrator made the episode a bit comical to his cohorts. Whalen and Helen tried very hard not to chuckle when they thought about the theft, or when Eric shuffled by, down the corridors of the theater. After swapping one-liners like, "Who would stoop so low?" Or, "You think Eric has any money left, or that he's a little short?" it was hard not to laugh, listening to Jans rant. But she did feel sympathy for her boss. Money remained tight, yet despicable Eric lumbering in and out below the doorknob, pushing up chairs to snoop around, painted a comical picture.

*

"Look at this, Helen" Whalen said on a late Sunday morning. The dancer leaned over, still holding her coffee cup with both hands, to glance at Whalen's newspaper.

"Sophie Tucker? Playing in Piccadilly?"

"There's a curtain at six this evening." He grinned, equally excited.

"I'll ring up Grace and Charlotte—they wouldn't want to miss this show for anything."

Noticing Harold Whalen looking oddly her way Helen explained, "I am a little star-struck over Sophie Tucker—I know that makes me sound like such an amateur." She shrugged her shoulders in confession.

This American singer known as "The Red Hot Mama," wasn't just a favorite of Helen's. The brassy singer enjoyed fame on both sides of the Atlantic. Just a chance to see her performance was a dream come true for the young American.

They arrived in Piccadilly at 5:30 PM, determined to find good seats for the 6:00 PM dinner show. Jans took charge, as usual, directing the host to place their party of five nearest the stage, while Helen scrutinized the dimly lit room, hoping to spot the star.

"That's her, over there" she whispered into Grace's shoulder, "I think she's greeting guests around the lounge. Let's get to our table." Helen watched as her idol moved among the guests, quietly chatting with patrons.

"Here she comes, act normal," the girl loudly whispered, the volume in her voice surprising her and earning a laugh from her friends.

"Now, where are you folks from?" Miss Tucker asked warmly, arriving at their table. Helen rose from her seat while blurting out "New York."

Whalen snickered. Miss Tucker smiled.

"Yanks?" the singer verified, appearing pleased to see folks from home. She sat at their table and gestured her accompanist to join them. During introductions the girl studied the celebrity. Taller and heavier than Helen expected, Sophie Tucker had blonde-reddish hair, beautiful skin, and a friendly expression. The star-struck girl couldn't keep herself from staring, especially when the legendary singer recognized that she had seen Helen and the boys at the Palladium.

"You three are very good. I enjoyed your performance enormously."

"Thank You, that's gratifying to hear from you," Jans smiled, pleased.

Still stealing glances at the icon, Helen had hoped to ask her friends about the old Mistinguett gang. She disciplined herself to focus her attention on Grace and Charlotte, catching only a few errant peeks at the famous American.

"I still don't understand. What brought you girls to London?" Helen lit her cigarette as she looked at Grace.

"We're booked to dance at the Savoy for two more months, and then Charlotte and I return to Paris," Grace explained. "And after Earl and the rest of the gang finish their shows, we are all sailing together to South America, of all places."

"What happened after I left? How long did you stay in the show with Miss?" Helen asked.

Charlotte spoke first. "By Budapest, all of us felt like you did. The time had come to leave—we had traveled long enough and no one wanted to travel any further east, especially with Miss so out of sorts."

"Things hadn't worked out for the Leslies either," Grace added. You remember Earl's so-called great job opportunity in Berlin?" she asked. Helen nodded, barely noticing when Sophie Tucker left the table. "German officials scared Earl and Carmen so badly that they quit and came back to Paris."

"The new government, under that Hitler character, does not approve of any entertainment that includes risqué material," explained Charlotte.

"So nothing funny," Helen dryly intoned.

"Right," Charlotte laughed. "Earl and Carmen began to feel like walking targets. The German police barged into their clubs, roughed up entertainers and employees, frightened patrons, then began to pay threatening calls on Earl at the central office in Berlin."

"He couldn't take it anymore and decided to resign. He and Carmen left without a backward glance. That country is no longer safe for anyone in our line of work," Grace concluded in a low voice. "So," she began again in a brighter voice, "that brings our story back to our plans for Paris and South America."

"We were hoping the club in Buenos Aires we're booked to play was a reputable establishment. But..."

Helen looked into her friend's face. "But what, Charlotte?"

Grace spoke up instead, confessing, "One part of the contract makes us both a little nervous. We had to sign an agreement to remain in the lounge area after our performances for the rest of the evening."

Charlotte continued, "It appears we were hired more for display than for our dancing."

Helen worked hard to keep a straight face, but knew their booking agency had breached an unspoken rule. Management had a responsibility to protect showgirls from inebriated patrons.

"Please don't tell your mother. Our mothers will find out and bring us home for sure. We have to accept these jobs, we have our mothers to support. Helen, you know there is nothing in New York," Charlotte said.

"I won't tell my mother, Grace, I promise."

Suddenly the room fell dark, startling Helen. Shifting her attention, the dancer watched as a spotlight revealed Miss Tucker walking to the microphone while her pianist played an opening flourish.

"Some of these days," Tucker sang in her deep alto voice. "You're gonna miss me, baby. Some of these days ... you're gonna feel you're so lonely."

The celebrated singer so captivated the girl that she forgot about the troubling conversation with her friends for the rest of the evening.

OBLIGATIONS

London
1934

"Whatever became of that Belgian boy, Helen? The one who followed you everywhere we played on the continent?" Charlotte asked as she again dealt cards around the miniature table in the Helen's room.

Grace and Whalen teamed together, while Charlotte sat in with Jans. All four arranged their cards during another quiet, layover afternoon.

"You mean Elie? Well, I'm not quite sure, Char," Helen replied, seated cross-legged on her bed, behind Jans. "He helped me in Paris, and stayed with me until my ship sailed from La Harve. Then he sailed to New York six weeks later."

"It sounds like he's pretty stuck on you. What part aren't you sure about?" Charlotte teased.

"I haven't heard a peep from him since I left New York. Not a letter, not a cable, nothing," Helen's brow wrinkled. "He mumbled some nonsense at the New York docks about never seeing me again, and that's the last he said to me."

"Do you like him? I mean, did you think you would end up married?" Grace distracted from her cards asked.

"I'm not sure," Helen honestly answered. "Elie has been such a constant in my life since we met in Brussels. But I can't say I like spending time with him like I should. He's a nice man, but I feel such relief when he leaves, not sad, as I should."

"Maybe it's for the best—not hearing from him, I mean," Grace said.

Helen stared at nothing. "Maybe."

After the men left the room, the girls lingered, chatting about other subjects in the small, warm room. Nostalgic, Helen felt like no time at all had passed since they roomed together under Mistinguett. After the evening ended, and her friends had departed, the girl prepared for bed. She recalled the camaraderie and joy of touring Europe with her friends. Musing, she soon saw herself moving on to Buenos Aires with the old team.

What if I changed my plans and joined Earl, Carmen and the girls in Paris? A reunion would be fabulous, she thought. Gnawing at her fantasy was the fact she had a mother in New York waiting for her. That detail sank her spirit, because she wasn't free to go. A sense of envy, of being left behind, stung a bit. Her people were traveling on without her. But, as she slipped into semi-consciousness, the idea of South America planted itself into her drifting mind—a viable alternative if things went badly after London.

*

Following the late curtain, the three Americans, Helen, Whalen and Harry Jans, lagged behind the parade of English cast members, heading to a pub for a post-show party. Making room under the new umbrella, Whalen ducked his head in next to hers, keeping dry in the dark downpour. Jans walked next to them under a dripping, black fedora, his dampened cigarette perched sportingly in his lips. As the throng of performers noisily invaded the pub, they shouted drink orders over each other, adding to an atmosphere of genial bedlam.

"Where should we sit?" the dancer wondered scanning the chatty, full tables.

"There's room at the end where Teddy's sitting." Whalen scouted, pointing across the smoky pub. The three New Yorkers' made their way over, dragging empty chairs from surrounding tables while Jans shouted for three glasses of ale.

Helen took a quick sip, swallowed, wiping foam from her upper lip, and then came right to her point. "My friends are heading to Paris, and then to Argentina, after the Savoy."

"Wow, that's some traveling. Charlotte and Grace, you say?" Whalen asked. She nodded her head. "They plan to see their share of the world, don't they?" he responded, impressed.

Jans, not fooled by her nonchalance, looked the girl directly in the eye. "Helen, Helen, Helen," he wryly began. "I know what you're thinking, but you do need to go home. Little girl, we have an agent in New York who plans to keep you as busy as you can stand." Whalen frowned, puzzled by Jans reaction, realizing more had been exchanged between the two than words.

Jans continued, "Your mother needs you, and Harold and I need you. South America can wait."

Finally catching on, Whalen added, "We just received a cable today that we are booked solidly with the Loew's chain through the fall and holiday season."

Helen took another sip from her pint. As she swallowed, a trace of self-conscious pink rose on her cheeks, "There's no fooling you, Jans. And I know you're right. My mother needs me. It's just the idea that they're free to go. But, I couldn't bear to leave you two." She winked. "Besides, who would keep Whalen in line? Still, I can't help but think, Harry, they're awfully lucky to travel and play together in Argentina."

*

"Beauty Sails into Port," *The New York Journal* announced, showing a photo of Helen in the paper's entertainment section. The shot focused on her shapely legs.

Photographers boarded the ship and prowled around the deck, plainly searching for someone. Helen, carrying her handbag and a small satchel scanned the crowds at the same time trying to locate her partners.

"You Helen Thompson?" asked a man who was clearly not a passenger. The girl looked the man over. He bore a blank expression, carried a large camera around his neck, and had a name on a badge pinned to his breast pocket.

"I am," she replied warily.

"I work for the *Journal* and I want to get a picture of you before the rest of these clowns do."

Surprised, then flattered, Helen spotted a handful of other, similar looking characters roaming the top deck. She quickly answered, "Sure, glad to."

A stroke of luck wearing my new suit, she told herself, pleased. Clad in a smart beige ensemble—a kick-pleated skirt, a fitted jacket trimmed in small cloth-covered buttons—she knew she cut a stylish image.

"Where would you like me to stand?"

"I don't. Hop up on that venting, and cross those pretty legs, honey."

Honey? I don't even know this guy. Pasting a warm smile on her face, Helen placed her right knee over her left and waved to the camera. All at once a half dozen or so lenses honed in on those same lovely legs in an explosion of clicks.

Before the photographer moved on to his next quarry, Helen stopped him. "Excuse me, but how did you know my name?" she asked, honestly puzzled.

"Hmm?" The cameraman absently grunted, loading a new roll of film into his camera.

"My name?" she repeated.

"Oh, all of us camera hounds get the passenger lists at the news desk before you people dock. We scare up the big shots for the paper's society page."

"Well, thanks." Helen honed in on the term, *big shots.*

True to the photographer's word, the following morning *The Journal* printed her picture. And as the camera had documented, the Jans and Whalen team had returned to New York, June 26, 1934 aboard the *S.S. Leviathan.* This surprise publicity gave Helen heart that perhaps New York had more to offer her than when she had departed.

Striding down the gangway Helen spotted her mother, nose-to-nose in an absorbed conversation with Carrie Whalen, Harold's mother. Standing apart from the older women stood Jans wife, Margery, waiting quietly alone. Instantly, cries of recognition erupted, hugs and kisses blended into the wider dockside reunion. Harry, after happily greeting his wife, tugged on Helen's elbow drawing her aside,

"Now don't sail away anywhere; I promise I'll be in touch soon. And don't get out of shape loafing around!"

Helen laughed. "Thank you again and again for bringing me along to London."

She then turned and stretched her arms wide and wrapped them around a surprised, blushing, Harold Whalen. "Will you still come by and help me with my hair?"

Whalen warmly hugged the girl. "Anytime, little one."

"We should be going, Helen," Bertha insisted. As the two waved goodbye, mother and daughter stepped into a cab and headed home to the Whitby Hotel.

*

With hardly time to unpack, the team indeed went back to work, appearing on the New York stage. *Variety* marked Jans and Whalen's return reporting, "Vaude is always dependable" at Loew's State, Broadway at 45th, adding as an illustration, "Jans and Whalen, with their pretty little blonde in black widow's weeds was a stunner. Dropping her bonnet and veil, the dress becomes quite enticing with a low back and yoke of net."

Reading the review the girl swelled with vindication by "good old" New York critics.

"I always thought it was funny," she muttered to Whalen, recalling the Palladium fiasco.

In October, the trio appeared before a full house prior to a premier of the film *Chained*, starring Clark Gable and Joan Crawford.

In one bit, the spotlight illuminated center stage where Harry sat on a step holding his ukulele. He began strumming and crooning, "All of Me, Why Not Take All of Me..." while Whalen and Helen entered the stage hand in hand. She pranced into a few delicate spotters, spinning up and down slowly like a merry-go-round. Meanwhile, Whalen tapped around her rotating counter clockwise, working his arms outward in contrast to Helen's vertical stance. As the ukulele played the last few bars, the two shuffled apart, and Helen blew Whalen a kiss across the stage. He mimed catching it in one hand and placing it on the ground. Whalen then imitated teeing off the kiss toward Helen like a golf ball. She caught the "kiss" and dramatically placed it on her heart, her eyes gazing upward. The bit ended with the ukulele and stage light fading, as the two strolled off-stage hand in hand. The audience shouted and clapped.

Later, as Helen was in her dressing room, she heard a knock on the door, followed by a voice calling, "Note for you, Miss."

"Just a minute," she shouted, pulling on a cream silk robe. Turning the knob, she faced the assistant stage manager holding a folded playbill.

"Thanks," Helen replied, studying the glossy paper, looking for writing. On the back, someone scrawled, "Enjoyed your act, young lady. Love to buy you a drink. Waiting in the lounge at the International Hotel across the street."

Glancing at the signature, she saw her admirer had only signed, "Charles."

"Charles, Charles, do I know a Charles?" She ran faces through her mind.

Turning over whether she should meet the admirer, she remembered the boys planned to go to the nightclub, too. If the guy got fresh they'd step in. So she dressed quickly and soon darted across busy Broadway to the International. Pushing through the heavy glass door, her eye caught a striking dark-haired gentleman who saluted her with his index finger beside his face.

"Charles?"

"Yes, please sit down, sweetheart."

"Thank you."

"What do you drink?" he asked, signaling the waiter.

"Bourbon and water, please," Helen answered, extracting a

cigarette from her brown handbag. Glancing up as Charles offered a light, she saw Jans standing at the bar with a shocked expression, frantically gesturing to her. Using his fingers, he cut back and forth under his chin. Helen didn't understand.

"Loved that widow act, very clever. But you're too young to even be married, right?" Charles asked.

She laughed, "It's just a bit I do."

"Well, you do it fine," he answered, while the waiter placed her drink before her on the white tablecloth.

"Where do you live, Helen?"

"Not far, The Whitby. Other side of Times Square."

"Ah, Midtown, this is a nice area."

At this Helen glanced again at her partner. Jans, his face more horrified, leaned in and spoke in Whalen's ear. Harold's face also appeared alarmed. Growing concerned, Helen made a little more small talk with Charles, finished her drink, bid him goodnight, and headed for the door. Coming so fast, she hardly saw him. Jans snatched her arm and doubled their pace to the sidewalk.

"Do you know who that man is, Helen?"

"He introduced himself as Charles," she answered.

"Yes, Helen, Charles 'Lucky' Luciano! Kid, he's a mobster!"

"Oh, Jans, you mean like Capone?"

"*Like* Capone? He's Capone's evil twin! I have to get you home." Harry pulled Helen down the block and summoned a cab.

The following morning a ringing doorbell woke her, and she heard her mother open the front door. A muffled exchange followed, ending with the door closing. Her mother's slippers padded down the hall toward Helen's bedroom.

"A chauffeur is waiting at the door and brought you this package. He says his boss would like to escort you to lunch."

Helen perched up on her elbows. "A gift? What kind of gift?"

"Helen, it's a Chanel purse; it looks expensive!"

Taking the box, she pulled off the rest of the gift wrapping. Inside she found a beautiful black patent leather clutch.

"Gee Whiz," Helen whispered.

"Who would send you such a costly gift? What haven't you told me?" Her mother's eyes narrowed, while she rummaged around in the tissue paper. Bertha extracted a card.

"Who is Charles, Helen?"

"Oh no. Mother, he bought me a drink after the show last night. Jans said he's dangerous, a mobster."

Bertha gawked at her daughter.

"I'm telling the driver you are unavailable. And I am giving him that thing back. Do you realize what it would mean to keep this? He'll claim you. You'll have an obligation to him. Bet he's married, too." Bertha shook her head in disgust.

Shaken, Helen handed over the box, hoping Luciano would understand her decline.

"Thank goodness for Jans warning." She shuddered.

*

Appearing at Loew's Palace Columbia, Jans and Whalen opened for a new Fox production, *The President Vanishes,* starring Edward Arnold and Janet Beecher. Energized by the theater's festive atmosphere, Jans peeked out from the curtain gesturing to his partners to take a glimpse.

"Natives are restless tonight, more a hive than an audience." He chuckled.

"They should be, it's New Year's Eve." Whalen lightly patted his back.

After the last curtain, the three, in buoyant spirits, met their friends and family at a dinner club off Times Square to welcome the New Year. Eileen joined them—Bertha and Carrie Whalen too, but the two mothers stayed only for dinner. Margery Jans greeted her husband with hug, and a young man, a dancer from a musical theater, came as Whalen's guest. At midnight the group toasted, hugged, and kissed as confetti, balloons, and tickertape fell from nets fixed to the ceiling. Jans tapped his glass with his salad fork, rose from his chair and proclaimed to the party,

"If you liked 1934, my friends, wait till you get a load of 1935!" Everyone clapped and laughed.

*

Helen was startled awake—the shrill ringing of the phone pulling her from a deep sleep.

"Mother?" the girl groaned. But the ringing persisted. Lumbering to an end table in the living room Helen lifted the receiver mumbling, "Thompsons."

"Helen, Helen!" The voice sounded distraught.

"Harold, is that you? What's wrong?"

"Jans quit the act. He told me he was through!" His voice broke, sobbing.

"How? When?" Helen gasped, as though slugged in the stomach.

"After you and Eileen left last night he became angry and stormed out of the club with his wife."

Helen, now fully awake, assured him, "He'll call today. I'm sure of it, Whalen. Whatever bothered him last night has certainly passed by now."

But Jans didn't call the next day, nor in the days following. And he wouldn't explain as Helen pleaded for answers when the two met for coffee.

"Nothing that concerns you, Helen," he answered curtly, closing the subject.

Bertha, of course, had her own opinion.

"Whalen has been the most supportive of you, and Harry Jans has treated him horribly. Of course you must remain with poor Whalen. Who's to say Jans wouldn't do the same when he no longer found any use for you."

In the end Helen remained with dear Harold Whalen in the painful breakup. Still grief stricken, he eventually forced himself from his bed, auditioned a few comedians, and added a new vaudeville partner—Russ Brown, forging the team of Brown and Whalen.

The new collaboration opened on the road, intending to polish the act before opening in New York. For Helen, the contrast between Jans and the new show was painfully clear. The magic of Jans and Whalen was missing, the chemistry gone. And the critics agreed.

"The performance was not quite up to the snappy standard of the old Jans and Whalen show," a *Variety* critic noted of the Baltimore performance. "The timing was too slow, the material too dated, and just wasn't funny. Brown pitched the joke setup with skill, while Whalen hesitated, a bit sluggish on delivering punch lines."

Helen didn't need a stage critic to tell her these problems— it was clear from her vantage point in the wings. Whalen had lost his confidence.

Variety concluded their dreary assessment in a final verdict, "The signature Jans and Whalen finale, the little song and dance skit made so famous by the old team, paled as it lacked Harry Jans and his famed ukulele."

Neither Helen nor Whalen ever mentioned the painful breakup with Harry Jans. Nor did the former partners ever speak again. Helen, though never one to burn her bridges with the Janses, remained especially close to fragile Harold Whalen. Yet, she also knew her time had come to move on from their partnership. She hoped her mother would see it the same way.

WEST PALM BEACH

Florida
1934

At first he told himself that Howard Hughes' good wages kept him in West Palm Beach. But Chum also knew his curiosity played a big part in remaining at the field. The famous tycoon was already a legend in aviation, as well as in motion pictures, and the young pilot had long admired self-made men. And though he looked forward to his new job, he was just as eager to watch the millionaire up close.

Over the next few weeks, Chum noticed that Hughes followed the same pattern each day. His driver motored up to the hangar in a Cadillac LaSalle, closely shadowed by another large Oldsmobile. The famed pilot stepped from the backseat, unfolding all six foot four inches of him. At same time, an entourage of followers poured out of the second car, casually circling the celebrity.

Chum also noticed that the aviator only spoke to his head mechanic, nodding frequently while he smoked a cigarette. Then Hughes and company inspected the rest of the facility—the tall tycoon facing the ground, continuing to acknowledge his lead man's comments.

If he looked up, Hughes sometimes nodded to Chum or to the other men in the hangar. Then with this morning ritual finished, Mr. Hughes and his retinue returned to their waiting cars and drove off to other unknown destinations.

On one especially stifling afternoon, Hughes unexpectedly turned up at the steamy buggy hangar, departing from his usual routine. Caught off guard, the crew quickly picked up their tools and bustled around, appearing busy. Hughes seemed not to notice.

Instead the famed pilot looked at his head mechanic and loudly announced, "These gentlemen and I," pointing to his cohorts, "are leaving for Los Angeles. Since that plane," Hughes stuck his thumb toward the Waco still on the tarmac, "was used, we will travel by rail." A few of the boys glanced Chum's way.

"Yes, sir, don't worry about a thing here, sir," the foreman answered. Hughes nodded again, and he and his associates left the field in a caravan of black autos.

"Wonder which beautiful actress Hughes is meeting." A young grease monkey sighed as he twirled a ratchet around his finger.

"Jean Harlow, you think?" said a kid still staring out the hangar doors.

"My money is on Paulette Goddard," added another, plunking coins into a soda machine.

"Back to work, boys." The head mechanic laughed. "We're not going anywhere."

Chum smiled. Just the phrase, "back to work," began to amuse him. As far as he could see the commotion was all "make work" instead of real industry. He was becoming restless from boredom.

After Hughes' dramatic exit, the crew mostly loitered around the hangar, sweating in the muggy heat—listening to the radio, smoking, sipping cokes, and playing cribbage. After a week of this meaningless inactivity, the young pilot, staring blankly into an immaculate engine, abruptly resolved, "As soon as I'm paid, I'm gone."

Three monotonous days later, Hughes and his party surprisingly reappeared at the field. The aviator had apparently changed his plans at the rail switching station in Jacksonville and never turned west. Still, Hughes' return made no noticeable impact, and the days continued to drag on: Cokes, cigarettes, cribbage, and heat.

While he was perched on a ladder examining another pristine Lycoming engine, Chum heard his name from across the facility.

"Over here," Chum called back, "Up on the ladder."

"Telephone call, buddy," a mechanic hollered. "In the hangar office."

"Thanks, JJ," he yelled, climbing down.

The voice on the line hollered, "Chum? That you, sport?"

Chum paused, trying to place the echoing but familiar voice. "It's me, boy, Hugh Perry."

Recognition lit Chum's eyes,

"Hey Mr. Perry, good to hear your voice. How are things up north?" Perry worked as the executive of sales for Waco Aircraft in Troy, Ohio, the company that manufactured his airplane.

"Well, now, I'm real good Chum, and business is pretty good. In fact, that's what I'm calling about."

Chum felt his pulse quicken. "What can I do for you sir?"

"You know, you did so damn good in that race and, well, would you be interested in working for us, Chum?"

Feeling his spirits begin to soar, Chum had to ask, "What would the job entail, Mr. Perry? Would you want me in Troy?"

"No, no, wouldn't do that to you, Chum, Troy is no place for a dapper gent like you," Perry chuckled. "We have this new model and there is some interest for it in South America. Smiling, Chum sensed the skies were opening and the archangels were tuning up a hallelujah chorus.

"That sounds real attractive, Mr. Perry. I think I would be interested in a job like that," even his voice smiled.

"And here I thought you would be all star-struck, slumming it with Howard Hughes," Perry laughed. "But when this position came up, your name was the first to come to mind. I thought I would give you first refusal."

"I'm glad you did Mr. Perry, and your timing is pretty good, I was thinking about a change anyway. Guess I miss my Waco," Chum laughed. But before hanging up, the young pilot suddenly wondered, "Mr. Perry, what equipment are the South Americans interested in?"

"Keeping up with our new aircraft are you, kid?" Perry sounded pleased.

"I guess I have, sir."

"Well, the Brazilians are very eager about a new fighter plane we've developed."

"A fighter?" Chum repeated, baffled.

"I know, I know—don't understand what they would need it for either."

Chum quieted in thought, wondering who could possibly threaten Brazil. "You still there, kid?"

"Yeah, Mr. Perry, I'm here. Just strange to imagine any South American trouble that would require machine gun strafing."

Shaking off that concern, Chum again became enthused. "You shipping the demo model to Roosevelt Field?"

"At the moment the plane's with the Navy. They want to test it, too," Perry explained. "Our agreement was three months for those flyboys to check it out. We'll ship it down to Rio de Janeiro after the military is done with it."

Chum hung up the office telephone, and stood motionless, absorbing this implausible change of fortune. Chum slowly walked out of the office, stopping to appraise the entire, immense working space.

Mechanics continued to poke around the equipment, the lead man in the far corner looked over a clipboard, a cigarette, ash dangerously angled, wedged between his right hand fingers. Silently, the young pilot made his decision and headed out the open hangar door, leaving behind Ailor's Waco Cabin, still parked to the side of the facility, and away from Howard Hughes and his West Palm interests. With a sense of elation, he cheerfully hiked the three miles to his hotel, collected his belongings, and caught a taxi to the train depot.

Restored, and back in control for the first time since the air race, Chum looked forward to returning to New York. The station, in contrast, was quiet—only a handful of passengers lounging on the wooden benches, while a couple of customers lingered at the ticket window. He joined the short queue to purchase his passage home.

So much had changed from the morning that Chum had forgotten to eat anything. His stomach sternly reminded him of his oversight. The pilot twisted onto a red stool at the station's empty lunch counter. Not bothering to look at the menu, he ordered a ham sandwich and a glass of root beer.

Even with his gurgling stomach, when his food arrived, Chum found he couldn't eat. The bread tasted fine, but the ham mulched around in his dry mouth. Giving up, Chum reached for the root beer, and soon joined the other passengers waiting on the benches.

At last the young man boarded the northbound, "Florida Special," to New York. As he settled in, viewing the passing scenery, Chum began to compile a list of loose ends to take care of before departing for Brazil. Mumbling he cataloged, "Sell my Chevy, see if Ailor will store my Waco, clean out the rest of my belongings from the Essex House and," Chum frowned, "Say goodbye to Frances, making her husband very happy. "And," he sighed, "I need to find time to see my mother."

He leaned his head back against the seat and soon started lightly snoring. But he didn't doze for long. His demanding stomach woke him up with a strong growl. Gathering his bearings, Chum stretched and wandered to the dining car.

RIO

1934

The trip by rail took nearly two days. When the train finally pulled into Grand Central Station, the young man grabbed his belongings and walked to the nearby Yale Club. There, he took a shower and changed into fresh clothes. Renewed, the pilot retrieved his car and possessions from the Essex House, and drove straight to Roosevelt Field. As Chum approached the low office buildings, he could see Ailor already standing at the office door, arms crossed, watching him. Chum could tell his benefactor knew about the new job.

"You are the only person I know who can fall into a pile of shit, and come out smelling like a rose," Ailor accused. Chum smiled.

"Crossing the Equator, Ailor, going south. But I need to ask you a favor," he began.

"I don't think a guy with your luck should get any more favors, Chumbley," Ailor tried to sound stern.

"I need a place to store my plane and wondered if I could use the hangar here," Chum asked, hoping to sound humble.

Ailor looked him over, "Sure Chum, it's a part of Waco lore now; we can show it off to paying customers."

Chum smiled again. He had forgotten his fondness for old Howard Ailor.

"And where the hell is my airplane? What is going on with that screwball, Hughes?"

"Ailor, I swear to you I have no idea what Mr. Hughes is planning. He most likely doesn't even know that I left. From what I saw at his field, he has probably forgotten the plane is still sitting there," the young pilot admitted defensively, feeling guilty.

"Well, Hughes better do something about that plane before

hurricane season," Ailor grumbled.

Chum suddenly changed the subject. "Ailor, I tried to call Frances from town, but no one answered. Have you seen her around the field?

"Kid, her husband, Marsalis, moved with her to Ohio."

"She's gone?"

"Yeah, Chum. I think he saw her drifting away and decided to get her out of town while you were in Florida," Ailor added.

"I would never have asked her to leave her husband, Ailor. Never. She was spoken for," Chum assured his friend, sadly.

"I guess Bill Marsalis wasn't so sure. She liked you an awful lot, Chum. Everyone could see it."

The young man's face became wistful. "You remember how competitive Frances could be with the other girls, especially Amelia Earhart?"

"Yep" Ailor chuckled.

"Frances always said Earhart's husband inflated her celebrity. She and I were always pleasant to Amelia and the other girls—I especially like Elvey, Betty and Edna Gardner."

"Those crazy girls" Ailor laughed. "The Ninety Nines. That collection of flyers might be more competitive than you bums."

Chum nodded, his eyes downcast.

In the weeks after his return, the pilot sold his Chevy to a photographer from the AP, removed the wings from his Waco, crating it in the hangar, and caught a train to Ohio, to the Waco factory in Troy, for a briefing on his new position.

Hugh Perry stood waiting on the windy platform at the Troy station, to shake the hand of his newest employee as he stepped off the train car.

"Welcome to winter in Ohio, Chum. Good trip, I hope?" Perry warmly asked, slapping Chum on the shoulder.

"Fine, fine, Mr. Perry. I've never been to Troy before. Sure off the beaten path, and cold," Chum affably ribbed.

"Well, it isn't West Palm Beach," Perry zinged in return, "and I'm not Howard Hughes!"

"Thank goodness for that." Chum joked. "Though he is quite a character, sir. But now that you've brought him up, I've changed my mind—Troy's more like paradise."

Chum and his new boss laughed.

In the following days the young man learned more about the new fighter plane and the ordering and shipping procedures Waco required. Finally, Perry directed Chum, "You go on down to Rio, get yourself a place to live, and get the lay of the land. As soon as we receive that fighter, the company will ship it down. Someone will cable you and let you know the arrival date. And kid, I'm glad you took the job; it's nice to have you on board."

"I'm glad too, Mr. Perry. Thanks, again. And thanks for tracking me down in Florida," Chum said, as he shook Mr. Perry's hand.

*

He joined the crowd on the dock in Brooklyn. But the throng dwarfed beside the massive size of the ship, which was painted a brilliant white with the name *Western World* emblazoned near the bow.

Chum moved up the gangway noticing that the vessel rested deeply in the saltwater. Chum's face betrayed his wonder—this was the first time he'd ever boarded a luxury ship. Stepping onto the top deck, Chum was met by a congenial steward who asked his name and destination.

"Mont Chumbley, Rio de Janeiro," he answered, hardly believing his own words.

A crewman scurried around the steward, politely inviting Chum to follow him to his accommodations. Gazing around in awe, the pilot followed, taking in all the ship's amenities.

Richly carpeted sitting rooms featured fireplaces. Passenger games like ring toss and shuffleboard were underway on the deck. Nearing the dining area, the young man spied a white terrazzo floor, furnished with black wrought iron and glass tables and potted palms.

Not bad for a farm kid from Virginia. Folks at home would never believe where I am right now, he thought. His earlier difficulties, the pointless hours wasted at Howard Hughes's hangar, and the news of Frances' move, were set aside. Only 25 years old and Chum felt back on top of the world.

*

Pulling back the sheer hotel curtains, the freshly arrived American surveyed the bright white sands of Copacabana Beach a floor below. An involuntary whistle passed through his lips, "Boy oh boy," he exhaled.

He watched as people romped on the sand and in the water—children patting full pails under their parents' watchful eyes, young people sunbathing or competing in friendly games. Pleased with all he saw, Chum marveled again at his good fortune.

Booked into The Hotel Gloria, the young man planned to find quarters more permanent, but this room far surpassed any place he'd ever called home. Unpacking his clothes, he decided to get in the shower before changing. Later, exiting his bathroom and toweling off his hair, Chum could see the afternoon light waning, his room dim in the growing shadows.

Once he dressed, the pilot left the hotel to stroll down a broad avenue parallel to the beach. Chum relished his dinner at a busy nearby eatery—beef in gravy, warm bread, and fruit. Strolling over to a brightly lit casino, he limited himself to only a few spins at the roulette table, and the happy new Waco representative headed back to the hotel, deciding to make it an early night.

"Bless you, Vickie," Chum whispered, opening an oversized yellow envelope the Waco secretary had forwarded to the hotel's front desk. Inside, he found driving directions to the field and government contact names, all listed with Portuguese pronunciations.

When Chum left the hotel lobby the next morning, the saturating sun momentary blinded him. Blinking, Chum hailed a taxicab, conveyed his destination to a Portuguese-speaking driver, and gazed out the window at the colorful city.

When the driver pulled up to the airfield, Chum paid his fare and easily found the Waco office. A rectangular sign, printed in English, "Western Aircraft Company of Troy, Ohio," was posted on the front of a low brick building. With his shoulder, Chum had to shove a wood door, warped and stained by the humidity and groaning as it gave way.

Moldy, stagnant air assailed him; gloom and the stench of mildew permeated the space inside. Chum propped open the heavy door and cranked open two glass jalousie windows on the back wall. Immediately, a pleasant breeze fluttered some paper on the desk. The young man set to work, inspecting the contents of the file cabinets and the desk drawers where he mostly uncovered minor damage inflicted by lizards and rodents.

"Need some poison and traps," he noted.

"Hey in there! You the new guy from Waco?" called a friendly voice from the entrance.

"Come in, come in. I'm Mont Chumbley, but please call me Chum."

Throughout the morning, American sales representatives stopped for a chat, drawn by the open door, all to say hello and welcome.

"My wife and I've been down here about a year and a half— we love Rio. Let's have a drink and I'll fill you in on the brass downtown," offered a rep from Stinson.

"Let me take you out to the clubs, Chum. The women here are simply beautiful," confided the fellow from Beechcraft.

Other sales reps from Fairchild and Stearman visited—all Americans, and all his rivals for Brazilian aircraft contracts.

It was mid-afternoon when Chum found his way to the Waco hangar which housed the company's demonstration aircraft. Changing into his mechanic's coveralls and battling mice and mold yet again, he quickly inventoried the planes inside and out. By 5:00 PM, he taxied up the runway for his first flight up—on the 4th of May, 1934.

Chum reveled in the airspace. Only water and mountains

dominated his surroundings. The vistas were breathtaking: Sugarloaf Mountain, a single rock protrusion rose from the bay, over to Corcovado Mountain, the site of the Cristo Redentor, Christ the Redeemer, who, palms up, blessed the pilot's maiden flight.

As he examined the landscape further, he could distinguish structures on the ground.

The city seems to flow everywhere, he marveled. Alcoves of houses, buildings, and roads, looked to Chum as though they'd spread like human lava around the rugged terrain. And the bay—so busy with both motor and sailing boats!

At sky level, the spellbound pilot saw other small aircraft also taking in the evening beauty. He watched as a bulging silver Zeppelin floated by, looking as if it were suspended by wires over the jagged mountains.

*

He was tired from worrying a good part of the night about this first call to the Air Ministry. Somewhere around 3:00 AM, the anxious pilot had gotten out of bed to look through his business folder again, thinking he should brush up on equipment options. But after one time through, Chum calmed down—he knew the information well. He returned to bed and this time slept soundly.

Emerging from a cab, Chum stepped through the grated iron doors of a resplendent ministry building, near Laranjeiras Plaza, thinking about sending some kind of gift to the resourceful and thoughtful secretary at the Troy office.

An impeccably attired military assistant met him in the lobby gesturing Chum into a brass cage elevator. Standing quietly, awkwardly, the American introduced himself. "My name is Mont Chumbley and I am the new Waco aircraft representative. I have an appointment with the Colonel." The military aide smiled in reply saying nothing. Continuing to smile Chum remarked, "And why you people need a fighter plane, I'll never understand."

Using more' gestures, the attaché guided the nervous young

American through a frosted glass door—the office of the Brazilian Air Ministry. Left seated in an anteroom, Chum quietly glanced around, examining framed pictures of pilots and aircraft. After a few moments the same aide motioned him to an inner office, where his first official sales meeting began.

The Colonel and his liaison relieved the young man's stress at once, addressing Chum in English, as did a number of other junior officers.

"This cabin model can carry airmail and passengers, and land on most airstrips," he proudly pointed out during his presentation.

"Yes, yes," responded the Colonel, "but Mr. Chumbley we have obstacles in the hinterland and require some, ah, defensive armaments."

"Well, of course the fighter should arrive any day, sir," Chum replied carefully. The models I can demonstrate now can be defended easily with small arms."

"Of course. I would look forward to a display of the cabin plane's capabilities. I shall visit your airstrip at your convenience. I have Thursday at 9:00 AM open, if that suits you."

Chum grinned, rising. "That is perfectly convenient. I look forward to hosting a demonstration, sir."

As the aide ushered the American out of the inner office, Chum noticed a surprised expression on the assistant's face. Despite the language impediment, Chum had to ask,

"Is something wrong? Did I say something improper?"

"No, Mr. Chumbley." The aide replied in clear English. Chum's face began to color remembering his remark in the elevator. "It is just that the Colonel has never traveled to your airfield before," the aide continued. "He sends subordinates. He must like you."

NEW FRIENDS, OLD FRIENDS

Rio
1934

"13 vermelho," he pointed for the roulette dealer. Looking up from the table he noticed two men around his age, watching and smirking. Chum grinned at them.

"Your Portuguese is horrible, you know that?" said one. He was an unusually tall guy, easily around 6'3" or more. *He's an American,* Chum registered.

"That may be true. But good enough that the dealer set my chips on the right spot," the young pilot countered, chuckling. The tall one laughed and spoke again,

"I'm Paul, Paul Youngs, and this Max Baer look-alike is Steve," he gestured with his shoulder to his darker, more muscled companion.

"Bancroft," added the friend.

"Mont Chumbley," Chum responded, placing his chips again on 13 red. "But you can call me Chum, everybody else does."

"Well Chum," began Steve, "if you can drag yourself from the roulette wheel, we can have a drink and preflight the showgirls in the lounge."

Chum grinned. "Sure, that sounds good. Let me cash these in," he said, nodding toward his winnings." The two young men waited while Chum redeemed his chips at the cage. Then he followed his new acquaintances into the lounge again, snickering at the one called Steve's intention to preflight the girls. Finding a table by the floor, the two men ordered highballs. Chum requested a beer. He looked at his tablemates and asked, "You two pilots?"

"Well, of course we are, Chum," replied Paul Youngs. "Steve and I both work for Juan Tripp; we fly Pan Am Clippers to the States."

"Ahh," the remarks about the girls now made sense, preflight—checking the outside of the aircraft before getting in the cockpit. He reddened a little extending the metaphor with females instead of planes. His new friends didn't notice.

"I just arrived in Rio, working for Waco Aircraft. I'm in talks with the military on a fighter they're interested in."

The Pan Am pilots nodded.

"I've heard something of that. There's an effort to open up the interior for airstrips, but the tribal people are resisting," Paul said.

"Yeah, I know. They mentioned *obstacles*." Chum pronounced the word with distaste.

Steve, returned to introductions explaining, "We're captains, Paul and me, on airboats and based here out of Rio."

"We have separate schedules, almost opposite really, but still with a lot of time off to catch some Brazilian sun," Steve added in an appreciative voice.

"Where you from, Chum?" Paul asked.

"Virginia, southwestern Virginia, my folks have a farm there," the young pilot answered.

"Couldn't resist cloud travel, huh?" observed Steve.

"Just wanted to see the world, not easy to do from a farm," Chum replied in a matter of fact tone. "How about you, Steve" he countered.

"Steve's a California boy," laughed Paul, "played for UC Berkeley in the '29 Rose Bowl."

Chum's eyes became big. "You played in that game? Against Georgia Tech?"

Steve wasn't too charmed at the turn the conversation had taken.

"Yeah, I was there. No one could stop that knucklehead Riegels, and it cost us the game." Chum knew the story. Roy Riegels had run the wrong way on the field, and nearly scored for the Yellow Jackets, before a teammate tackled him on the three-yard line.

"You were there, huh? Bum luck, 8 to 7 loss," the athlete in Chum was sympathetic. The three spent the rest of the evening talking sports, Rio, and aircraft until Chum announced he needed to get to bed.

"You want to meet us at the beach tomorrow?" Paul Youngs asked.

"Maybe, Paul. What time are you thinking?" he asked, reviewing his schedule in his head.

"What do you say we plan about two o'clock, here, beachside of the casino?" Steve suggested.

"Sounds good to me," the young man brightly answered.

On the following afternoon, Chum donned swimming trunks, a beach jacket, and shoes. On his way out of the hotel, he stopped by the front desk and asked, "Any messages for Chumbley?"

A crisply dressed clerk courteously handed him a telegram. Postmarked New York, Chum wondered what Howard Ailor could possibly want. Breaking the seal he read

"Air show accident. Dayton. Frances killed. Sorry kid. Ailor"

A sensation like a strong ocean wave crashed against his knees. He needed to sit down. He collapsed onto a nearby chair. *Frances dead? How? She knew how to fly.*

The young man remained frozen for nearly an hour, staring at the slip of paper. Finally a voice interrupted his thoughts. "A drink, sir?"

He glanced up with a start, to see a smiling hotel waiter, then to his watch. "Oh, no. No thank you."

He decided to press on with his afternoon plans. However, before leaving the lobby, Chum walked to the front desk and dispatched a cable back to Ailor requesting details—and thanking Ailor for letting him know.

He left the hotel and started down the mosaic-adorned sidewalk. Fountains sprayed in pulsating beauty to his left, Royal Palms provided welcome shade to his right. Chum didn't notice.

Though he had been hungry earlier, the warm smells of beef, bread, and spices no longer drew him. Through open air eateries, patrons enjoyed rice and beans—enormous plates holding robust portions of beef, stewed in gravy with bread.

Had he the presence of mind to notice, Chum may have registered his hunger. Facing forward, squinting into the blinding light of beach and sky, he directed his feet onto white sand, toward the water. He then heard his name, looked to his left and sure enough Paul was waving his long arms. He resolved to put aside his grief for the moment.

"The game is called Pataka," Steve explained as Chum took a spot next to him. The Americans faced a team of equally resolute Europeans.

"They are about to hit that little beanbag our way, and we can't let it touch the ground," Paul directed. "We can't let these jokers beat us."

"What's the best way to bat it? Open handed? Underhand? Overhand?" Chum asked.

"Open handed, but other than that, any way you can get to it," Steve instructed. With no net the two teams batted the little orb, crashing into each other, rolling in the sand, leaving Chum thoroughly entertained at the fierce competition.

As the afternoon sun settled closer to the western mountains, the three flyers wandered to an outdoor *Boteco* for a cold *chope*. Enjoying their beer and Brazilian beef stew, Steve seemed anxious to say something.

"Chum?" he began, then noticed his new friend's distraction. He repeated, "Chum?"

"Yeah, yeah, sorry Steve," he replied.

"Listen buddy, we have a third bedroom at the apartment that is crying out for another pilot."

Chum looked at his new friend replying, "You do, huh?"

"We've been talking, Paul and I and ... where is it you're staying right now?" Steve quizzed.

"I'm at the Gloria," Chum responded, pointing with his thumb in the direction of his hotel.

"We wondered if you would be interested in our spare room."

"Well, yeah, Steve. I needed to get looking for a place and that would, well, be terrific," he faintly smiled.

Paul remarked, "We didn't think you could pass up a good deal."

Chum's new apartment, number 404, proved to be a therapeutic change, with a better view of the beach than the Hotel Gloria, and only a block from the Casino Copacabana. And best of all, he found good company in Steve and Paul.

*

The reflection in the mirror wasn't what the pilot wanted to see. "I look more a hundred years old than twenty five," he lamented.

Howard Ailor had mailed a packet to Chum filled with newspapers clippings, all covering Frances' death. It was at an air show in Dayton, Ohio where she had met her demise rounding a pylon. Another flier, Edna Gardener Whyte crowded Frances too closely, accidently clipping her right wing. Off balance, her wing hit the ground, the plane cart-wheeled, killing the girl. Ailor had added a personal note describing the funeral held at Roosevelt Field.

> *The service was real nice, Chum, you would have approved. Her casket, covered in flowers, sat in the center of the hangar. Two Wacos were parked on either side, propellers facing her in tribute, and we all gathered around for the service. Everyone was there. Even Perry flew in from Troy. I saw Amelia and Betty—nearly all the Ninety-nines attended, (I heard Edna has taken to her bed in grief). Bill Marsalis stood with his hands on the casket and wept. I felt sorry for the guy. I know you would've liked to have been here, but it's probably better that you're busy down there.*
>
> *Ailor*

The Hiram Walker rep had given the pilots a barrel of scotch for their apartment. Finishing Ailor's letter, the young man toyed with pouring himself a stiff one and drinking away his pain. But, never one for hard liquor, he knew the alcohol would just make him feel worse. Instead he sped out to the field for an extended flight.

*

Most days, Chum could be found at the beach or on the golf course, that is, after a morning of working at the ministry or airfield. Wholly conscious of his good life, he never forgot his mother was the one who had made it all possible for him. It gnawed on him that Martha still lumbered back and forth to an old outhouse, in all weather, in all seasons. Her kindness had brought her few modern conveniences. Electrical lines had not yet reached southwest Virginia, so she didn't have electricity. And her occasional, cheerful letters from the farm amplified his burden of prosperous guilt.

"Hey, Chum. Heading to the field?" Steve Bancroft asked, as the Waco rep sat down to a bowl of fruit and toast.

"You just fly in Steve? You look beat," Chum noticed, glancing at his friend.

"I did, indeed. I'm just going to grab some food and head to bed," Bancroft yawned, stretching out his arms, cracking his shoulders back.

"So what's new in the big city?" Chum asked.

"*New York Times* right there, Chum. I'm going to sleep."

Reaching across the table with his left hand, while spooning in a mouthful of bananas with his right, he read the headline, "Congress Implementing a Rural Electrification Act." Drawn to the story he read the entire article.

On his way to the field, Chum stopped at the Western Union Office to send a telegram: *Mother- Wire the house for lights through the REA. I will pay cash. No government loans. Please respond. Mont.*

Chum later sent her the funds for the work and soon learned that electricians had completed the job. Once the wires were spliced to power lines strung east from the Tennessee Valley Authority dams, Martha's customary darkness finally turned to light. Merely by snapping a switch, the farm moved into the 20th Century. Satisfied he'd improved her life Chum sat down and wrote her a long happy letter.

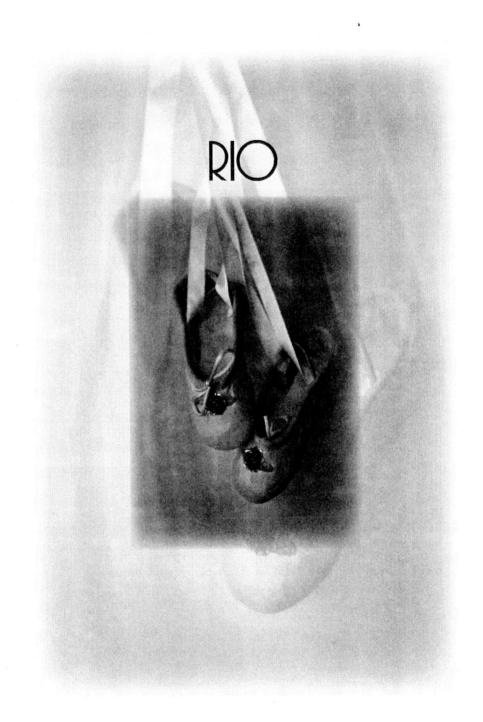

RIO

1936

The radio purred Eddie Duchin's sweet rendition of, "I Only Have Eyes for You."

Helen sat sideways across a wingback chair, legs nervously scissoring over the armrest, betraying her tension. In her hand she held the source of her discomfort—a surprise letter from her Belgian admirer.

"Well—well," she sighed again, confounded. "Seems as though Elie hasn't moved on after all."

Bertha was gone, so Helen had collected the mail downstairs. Flipping through the letters in the lobby, she had felt a surge of anxiety as a small grid of European stamps caught her eye. Staring at the envelope, she slowly mounted the stairs, dragging her feet.

Back in her chair, Helen had reached for her pack of Chesterfields and matches. Striking the cigarette, she had inhaled deeply, still dubiously eyeing the envelope. After a few moments, she surrendered with a deep sigh, and slit open the onion-skin missive, her fingers slightly shaking.

The Belgian began in a detached tone, relating his business and travel plans and some of the issues holding him in Brussels. Relieved, she scanned ahead, finding nothing too troubling. Elie had tried to travel to Germany to meet with investors, but those plans had fallen through:

> It appears that the political climate has so deteriorated in Berlin, my potential partners were forced to withdraw their financial interest.

Helen, still calm, continued on, finally reaching the words she had prayed weren't there. *Why do you write to me in such formal terms? I would like to convey in my letters more endearing terms, but reluctantly restrain myself.*

"Oh boy, there it is," she whispered. "I guess I'm still his girl."

Clasping the letter in one hand and her cigarette in the other, she stared at nothing, until a clear thought burst through, *He's going to ask me to marry him! More endearing terms? When did I ever say I loved him? Why did Elie have to become so serious? So possessive? Even Grant had the self-respect to give me time. How do I end this?*

Helen sat back, staring at the ceiling, wondering why a romance never blossomed, why she felt so uncomfortable with Elie. *We have never shared a laugh together. I've never, ever heard him tell a joke, or let loose and have fun. Now that I think of it, all he ever seemed to want to do is stare at me. I can't recall any serious conversation about a movie, or a news event. He's only interested in Polyphoto and staring at me.*

"The relationship is all in his mind," she realized, thinking aloud. "That's got to be it. He thinks he loves me and we're not even friends."

And a week later Elie, indeed, proposed in a flowery, formal letter.

"I am overjoyed to say the words so long in my heart," he wrote.

Helen ran her fingers across the thick, expensive stationary. Wearily she looked at her anxious mother, "At least he's across the Atlantic and not across the kitchen table."

*

"Every time I come back to New York, I feel like I'd do better elsewhere!" Helen griped to her sister as they walked to the Roxy Theater. "Getting noticed here, in the city, is as impossible as it gets. Either I throw myself in front of a trolley car for a headline, or it's time for a drastic overhaul of my career!"

"Alas, you're not considering leaving poor mother again, are you?" Eileen devilishly asked with false concern.

"That's not funny, Eileen. Leaving New York is never easy."

Eileen spoke again more seriously. "I know things are difficult right now, just try to stay close as long as you can, Sis. Bertha gets so despondent when you're away."

"I'll try," Helen shook her head doubtfully. "I suppose it's still possible I could get some kind of break here."

Trying to keep her word, she answered an open audition for famed Broadway composer Billy Rose. Helen towed her mother along for this call, both women giddy to catch a glimpse of the famed showman. And though her performance seemed to go all right, she never got a call back. Still, grateful for the opportunity, she shrugged, *At least I can tell my great grandchildren I once auditioned for Billy Rose.*

Each morning, she spread theatrical papers across the living room floor, and continued her daily search. On her hands and knees she scanned the classifieds, listening to the radio, ashtray smoldering, running her index finger down the inky columns. Helen had noticed and passed over an ad for Lyons & Lyons Inc., a talent firm in the Paramount Building on W. 43rd St. This particular morning, she stopped.

"Maybe an agency is what I need," she said suddenly, impulsively reaching for the telephone. "No one else looks to be beating down my door."

A day later, Helen stepped from a crowded elevator into the firm's hectic fourth floor office. Photos of celebrities were splashed across the walls, and the desks were filled with busy secretaries. Before long, Helen was shaking the hand of friendly Mr. Lyons, who placed her confidently at ease.

The Lyons firm soon came through with three solid bookings. Helen appeared first with, "The Harry Carroll Revue," at the Chez Samakann, and at another theater, the Chez Paree. Those two jobs led to a guest spot with New York radio host, Matty Levine offering Helen the chance to sing on-air.

Standing, facing the microphone, watching for the cue light, Helen cringed as the host announced,

"I'd like to introduce a lovely young miss, Helen Thompson. I hate to brag, but I heard this sweet little thing at the Chez Paree, and had to have her on the show." Levine cooed on in his deep soothing voice. "She's something of a 'new find' of mine. She is fresh to New York, so let's give a warm Manhattan welcome, for Miss Helen Thompson."

She rolled her eyes at his inaccurate hyperbole, but Levine never noticed. Moving closer to the microphone, she took a measured breath and began,

> *You're the Top, You're the Coliseum,*
> *You're the Top, You're the Louvre Museum...*

Her body started swinging to the rhythm of the piece. Barely restraining herself from breaking into dance, she brought the song home with style.

> *But if baby I'm the bottom,*
> *But if baby I'm the bottom,*
> *But if baby I'm the bottom,*
> *You're the Top...!*

She extended the last note with power, while the horn section caught the spirit and improvised a counter-flourish.

As Helen finished singing, those in the studio enthusiastically applauded. Helen gratefully grinned, thinking, *I need to sing more often.*

After Christmas, the sisters, together, danced at the Roxy Theatre into early 1936. Helen didn't particularly care for the place, mostly due to Maria Gambarelli pictures featured on every wall.

"That woman took us to Europe and then left us," she pointed out to Eileen. "Her royal highness!" she scowled.

From the Roxy, the sisters played the Paramount Theatre in Newark for another four-week engagement. Helen grew increasingly dissatisfied with each curtain.

Sleep began to elude the girl. She fell into a habit of lying stiffly on her narrow bed, listening to Eileen's rhythmic breathing across the little room.

How do I break out of this rut? She fretted. Running a torrent of options through her head only pushed sleep further away.

My name was printed next to Chevalier's, her mind silently shouted. *He flirted with me—I appeared before him on the playbill. I liked that type of celebrity; I want that for my career.*

Staring blindly into the dark, Helen sat up, drawing her knees tight. "There is only one thing I can do," she murmured, "Catch a boat and sail away from here."

Terrified to say anything to Bertha, she decided to research overseas opportunities. Her friends at the firm on 43rd street became her natural first stop.

"Mr. Lyons what contacts do you have for work south of the equator?"

"None, I'm afraid, Helen. South America is out of our booking region. Now we could set you up nicely for Canada, particularly Quebec if you like," Mr. Lyons encouraged.

"Oh, well, thank you for that offer, but I'd prefer to go south. Who do you think might help me?" she inquired a little disappointed.

*

"No, it can't be him, not Jack Miller!" she muttered stomping down 43rd Street. But it was all too true—an old agent Bertha had found years before, Jack Miller, was the only manager booking South American clubs. Bertha adored him. Helen didn't. *That man sent me practically to Nome, Alaska, and to the seediest joints imaginable. I wouldn't take off my shoes in some of those flea-bitten dives,* she shuddered, remembering. But after looking around, it turned out Miller, indeed, ran the only agency booking entertainers in Brazil and Argentina.

Meeting with Miller in his office, Helen was rather surprised by Jack's newfound professionalism.

"Since you called me, I've been looking around a bit," Miller began. "By the way, how is your mother? What a nice woman. Tell her hello for me, Helen, will you?"

Helen impatiently prompted the agent. "She's fine, Jack, thank you. So what did you find out?"

"Yes, yes." Miller continued. "A Brazilian promoter, a man named Max Koserin is quite interested in you. He liked what I told him of your background, and your experience. He's authorized me to make you a contract proposal. Look it over, kid, and tell me what you think."

Surprisingly giddy, the dancer sashayed out of the agent's office repeating, "Eight weeks at the Casino Copacabana in Rio, with another possible four-week option in Buenos Aires."

She couldn't have dreamed of a better arrangement. Miller didn't say exactly where she'd play in Argentina, but Helen, ecstatic at that moment, didn't care.

Prancing, the girl reveled in her good fortune. But as she turned the corner onto 44th street, her feet began to grow heavy, trudging up to the Whitby. Her joy trickled away as she realized that she had to tell her mother the news.

"Convincing Bertha to see the value of this tour will take a minor miracle," she said with a sigh. Plodding up the stairs, Helen, stomach all in knots, pushed open the door.

"Mother...Bert? I have good news," she quavered uncertainly.

Down the hall she could hear Louis Armstrong quietly singing "I'm In the Mood for Love," on the radio.

The girl was shocked and relieved when the discussion passed a lot more smoothly than she believed possible.

"Well, Helen, we do need the money, and heaven knows nothing is happening in New York. Jack wouldn't steer you the wrong way," Mother added in a satisfied tone. The girl's mouth hung open at Bertha's surprising support.

"Besides I think that I might just follow you down. I could use a pleasant vacation. I always liked that Jack," she mumbled.

Watching Bertha's face, Helen began to unravel her mother's change of heart. As always, in the back of mother's mind, the "big break," would happen at any time, but not in New York. On that point, both Helen and her mother were of one mind. This sojourn south could be the big opportunity mother and daughter had always desired.

*

"Why today, Elie! Why did this have to arrive today?" Helen cried out exasperated, as her eyes raked over the Belgian's elegant script.

> *Honestly, were it not the picture you gave me in Brussels at the outset of our meeting I should have forgotten what you looked like…I am, and have been all along, very hurt at your silence, also at the matter-of-fact and business-like phraseology used in your letters.*

Of course he was right, and his chiding began to douse her cheerful mood. Helen placed his chastising letter in her bureau drawer, determined to resume her sunnier itinerary for the day. She had many stops to make around the city.

The dancer first stepped into the end of a line that was thankfully moving quickly. Before long the dancer faced a frosted, glass window etched "New York City Department of Health." Inside the portal waited a weary-faced clerk, impatiently tapping a pencil.

"I am traveling to Brazil for work, and need a health certificate for my visa," she chanted. Before long, Helen was ushered into an examination room where a staff physician checked her out. He took her blood pressure and pulse, looked in her ears and into her throat, and listened to her heart. That was all.

Placing the certificate in her handbag, Helen confidently moved on to the New York Police Department. Again she recited, "My name is Helen Thompson, and I must obtain an affidavit to travel abroad for work."

This stop made her unnecessarily edgy. Helen fidgeted, checking her wristwatch, and she caught herself rubbing her sweaty palms together. Nervously she watched as policemen passed in and out of the cavernous sea-green headquarters. With a bobbing foot keeping time over her crossed leg, Helen counted the minutes until a uniformed sergeant called her to the booking desk. She smiled, looking at her spotless affidavit, and glanced up just as the officer gave her a flirtatious wink.

Paperwork in hand, Helen took the subway downtown to 17 Battery Place, the home of the Brazilian Consulate. An accommodating official asked Helen to sit for three snapshots for their records, and stamped her documents, quickly clearing the eager young dancer to work in Brazil. Thoughts of Elie's reproachful letter were more than forgotten.

The night before Helen sailed, Bertha tried to contain Helen's bubbly enthusiasm by listing strict rules for her to follow while out of the country.

Never meet with a boy alone.

Do not get involved with any boy in a show.

Find a friend and stick close to her.

Return to your dressing room immediately after your final bow.

Helen took her mother's fretting in stride, amused at how conveniently Bertha had forgotten that she'd already been away, twice, to Europe and England. She affectionately placated her mother in her first letter home:

> *I'll do everything you told me and I won't do anything you told me not to do, (guess that covers everything).*

After four days at sea, *The Southern Cross*, a Munson Line steamer, made its first routine stop in Havana, Cuba. Helen stood on the deck with another Koserin dancer, her cabin mate, Lila, watching as the harbor drew closer. Once dockside, the crew directed the lively flow of departing and loading travelers who were bustling up and down the crowded passageway. Seagulls and egrets swooped and perched on pylons, waiting for errant tidbits from the galley, while mail bags were dropped off and collected from Cuban postal officials.

Helen, who had letters going out, waited in a crowded queue outside the ship's mailroom for some word from her family. The clerk handed the girl the two letters she expected, but a third, a neatly typed envelope from Brussels slid out from between.

Helen, pensive, found a deck chair and sitting, opened her admirer's first, to get it out of the way. The Belgian began by describing his travel plans across the Atlantic.

"I plan to traverse across Canada by rail and make my way to Japan and hopefully beyond conducting Polyphoto business."

She mumbled, "He certainly has every stop detailed on this trip— Montreal, Winnipeg, Vancouver ..."

Further on, Elie related that he was next crossing the Pacific via Hawaii to his destination Kobe, Japan where, *I plan to negotiate a large contract with investors in that city.*

But she couldn't help but flinch when he added:

> *I hope that the Japanese war on China, or you, will not impede my efforts in any way. I am, myself, ashamed at the sort of letters you compel me to write to you and which, Lord knows, I should have preferred to couch in more endearing and loving terms...I was so disappointed that, when a few days ago, the opportunity presented itself for me to sell my interest in Polyfoto for the USA. I took it or should I say, grabbed it, as I was not anxious to proceed again or live in a country which had brought me so much unhappiness and disillusions."*

"Good lord, Elie. I've never made any commitment to you," she whispered with a heavy heart. "You are free to go or to do whatever you choose."

Placing the Belgian's letter on her lap she stared out to the dark, murky water. She knew he was trying to influence her with guilt. *Elie expects that I will meet him in Montreal or Toronto. He has to know I won't go. Even if I were in New York I wouldn't go. He must know that by now.*

Forcing herself to tuck away her Elie problems, Helen decided to read her other mail. However, the Belgian wouldn't be denied.

"Elie wrote to me a very nice, but sad letter," Bertha began, "I thought I ought to send the note on to you."

"When does that man have time to run his business?" Helen exclaimed, flabbergasted. Steadying herself again, Helen confronted Elie's neat, cursive script.

I have written once or twice to the addresses you gave me and am wondering if Helen is actually getting my letters...somehow I am beginning to wonder if my prophecy to her, on the night prior to her sailing for Europe, that we shall never meet again is not actually coming true... one cannot really say that I am meeting with luck or even encouragement where the likelihood of she and I ever getting together is concerned.

Closing her eyes, Helen felt the tears rise from somewhere deep. She wept, not only out of her powerful resentment toward Elie, but out of her own shame, as well. After a truly cleansing breakdown, Helen was finally all cried out. She blotted her nose and wet eyes admitting, "By doing nothing, I have unkindly led the man on."

MR. KOSERIN

South Atlantic
1936

Aside from the never-ending Elie issue, the voyage itself passed pleasantly. Helen and Lila scrambled out of their beds each morning ready for fun. They hurried to breakfast in the dining room, joining the other young people on the ship. And depending on their moods, Helen and her cohorts played shuffleboard, ping-pong, or other games on deck. After meals she strolled with Lila around the upper level, and the girls always found time to take in the afternoon sun.

Helen enjoyed the scenic two-week voyage, which included additional ports of call along the way, for passengers and mail. Helen noticed that each time they docked, *The Southern Cross* steered into harbors increasingly clogged with more ocean-going traffic. Recife, in particular was congested enough the ship had to sit off shore until its scheduled arrival time. Anxious for Rio, Helen asked a crew member why the ship had to sit and wait.

"Must keep to the timetable, Miss. The cost of coming into port early can be as high as $500 a day."

After another stop in Vitorio, the ship downshifted to a veritable crawl. She could feel the air thicken, heavy and muggy, in the motionless heat. Sweltering, the two American girls grew impatient with the slower pace and filled their time packing then repacking their trunks.

The last night on board, Helen took her time washing and setting her hair. She had painted her nails and toes a bright red, and had gone to bed early; 8:00 PM. Lila did the same. The day before, during lunch, an elderly lady from Connecticut had described the beauty of approaching Rio by sea.

"There is no panorama more exquisite than entering Guanabara

Bay at sunrise," the matron declared, her eyes bright with enthusiasm.

Their curiosity piqued, the girls thanked their luncheon partner, and agreed to greet the dawn as it lighted their nearly mythical destination.

The deck appeared empty, dark, and still just before 4:30 AM. The girls had stumbled out of their beds, pulled on their robes, and stepped out into the cool air. As Helen's eyes adjusted, she could identify other early risers, also clad in their robes. Clustering at the railing, the onlookers were absolutely overwhelmed with the panorama that gradually unveiled before them.

Helen gazed as the sun, rising from behind her, shadowed an elongated silhouette of the ship on the quiet water. Sugar Loaf Mountain presented slowly, from the summit down, exposed by the rising light, cobalt and gold reflecting on the calm, glassy bay. The relatively dry morning air and growing excitement over their imminent departure from the ship left both girls exhilarated.

"Lila, this was a keen idea!"

"Sure was. Glad I thought of it," Lila replied, laughing.

*

Helen's intuition alerted her that something wasn't quite right. Standing behind Lila, in the customs queue, she watched as a short, balding official approached them from the head of the line. He tapped both girls on the shoulder, gesturing for them to step off to the side.

Innocently, she and her friend complied, dragging their trunks and pulling smaller bags with them. The official then returned to the front of the passageway without a word. The two girls looked at each other, puzzled at the strange request. There seemed to be no special reason they were targeted, and no one who bothered to provide them with an explanation.

The Club Copacabana manager, Mr. Max Koserin arrived to the docks to personally pick up his American dancers around 10:00 AM. He smiled at his new employees, whom he noticed at once.

His expression shifted dramatically, however, when he realized they were standing alone, outside of the customs queue, with their baggage at their feet.

"Good Morning, ladies. I presume that you are Miss Thompson and Miss Hart?" Koserin asked.

Helen spoke first. "Yes. I'm Helen, and this is Lila. Thank goodness you're here, Mr. Koserin. That man at the front pulled us out of line without telling us why. We don't understand what's going on."

"Please try not to worry," their new boss assured, looking them both in the eye. "I will get to the bottom of this unfortunate misunderstanding."

Koserin walked to the customs officer and began what quickly escalated into a heated exchange. Helen felt her hope for a quick resolution fade.

"This gentleman has informed me that the city of Rio has recently passed an ordinance requiring all foreign acts coming into the city to deposit a bond with the police," the club manager explained when he returned.

"We have to...?" Lila began to cry out.

"No, no, my dear, that is my job," Koserin soothed the frightened dancer.

Mr. Koserin explained that the sum required for their bond totaled the entire eight-week salary for both girls, paid in advance. Strangely, Helen again became calm when the manager didn't blink at the so-called "news." In fact he showed no surprise at all. She guessed he expected the snag.

Still, he turned to the girls and cautioned, "Please do not worry, I will be back."

Lila opened her mouth to speak, but Koserin raised his hand, continuing, "It will take most of the day to generate that sum of money. Stay together and please don't be alarmed."

Koserin smiled serenely and then departed.

Again watching the little bald bureaucrat, she noticed that he barely glanced at the passports of travelers he was processing. She quickly understood that the two of them were victims of petty corruption. No actual protocols existed for performers or any other workers to enter the country. She recalled her trips to the police station and consulate in New York, now wondering why she had bothered.

As the day dragged on, Helen grew more certain that their new boss' presence wasn't just limited to a warm welcome and a lift to their hotel. She believed that Koserin had rescued other new acts delayed the same way. And though she trusted that he would return with their affidavits, it didn't help that both girls were stranded in the heat and humidity. No one offered them a chair, a drink of water, shade, or any help. The two Americans just stood miserably under the Rio sun.

When Lila meekly asked, the chief steward refused to permit them to go to their compartment to wait out of the heat.

Wiping her forehead with a handkerchief from her purse, Helen sighed. It had been hours, and there was no sign of Mr. Koserin with their ransom. Her eyes, automatically raked the docks searching for their boss, then toward the departing passengers. It was at that moment Helen locked eyes with the bullish little customs agent.

"That official over there, do you see him? Helen whispered to Lila.

"The man who pulled us out of line?" Lila asked.

"Yes, him." He keeps leering at me. It's been getting worse the last hour or so."

"Disgusting!" Lila scoffed.

"I wonder how often that little twit gets away with his scheme," Helen quipped. Both girls shuddered, glancing again toward the toad-like bureaucrat.

Time ground on and they watched as a queue of new passengers began boarding from the dock below.

Observing the foot traffic Helen realized, "Lila, I think we have another problem. This ship is scheduled to leave for Buenos Aires at five o'clock." Swallowing her panic she added, "And we're going too, if this problem isn't resolved."

Out of the corner of her eye she caught the official again, grinning suggestively. Tears traced down Lila's pink, burning cheeks.

Turning away, glancing automatically toward the dock, Helen gasped as a throng of newspapermen and photographers swarmed up the passageway. "Someone's tipped a Rio newspaper. We're news, now."

Reporters crowded around their trunks, shouting in Portuguese, vying for a story or photo of the two trapped American starlets.

Lila, wet-eyed, stared ahead, not acknowledging the cameras or chaos. Helen, feeling protective of her new friend, held up one hand, blocking the mob, while placing her other arm around her distressed friend. Beginning to lose her own composure, she glanced again from her wristwatch to the dock, as Mr. Koserin suddenly appeared. He had finally returned. Striding with authority up the passageway, carrying papers above his head, Koserin presented two affidavits of money placed with the local magistrates.

"I have never been so happy to see someone in my life!" Helen laughed, now equally as teary eyed. Truly, for both girls, Koserin was a sight for sore eyes. The manager glared coldly as the disappointed official shrugged, accepting the documents—releasing the Americans to enter the city.

After the all-day ordeal the two demoralized girls descended the passageway with their benefactor. Helen asked Koserin for only one kindness, "Could we please have a drink of water?"

*

Escorted by their boss, the spent newcomers were chauffeured through the unfamiliar city. The girl stared wide-eyed at the extraordinary mass of humanity. Swarms of people filled the sidewalks, overflowing into the streets. Bicycles maneuvered through running children, street vendors, shouting pedestrians, and honking cars. Warm air swept back Helen's hair while she, fascinated by the sights, motored through.

Koserin made a quick turn, and the girl saw a fortress of

mountains. "Miss Helen," her new boss explained, "that is the famous Christ of the Andes. Is it not magnificent?"

"Magnificent," Helen murmured.

Navigating expertly through the impossible traffic, Mr. Koserin tried to point out other notable spots. Finally the weary girls stumbled out of their new employer's sedan. While bellmen collected their luggage, Koserin stepped from his car calling, "Ladies, please consider joining me for dinner tonight, we have much to discuss."

A bit dazed, the girls glanced at each other, with Helen recovering first. She replied, "That would be lovely. What time were you thinking?" hoping he planned a late supper.

"I will come around at 9:00 PM. You can meet me right here," Koserin said.

Both girls smiled, genuinely this time. In their room, the two tired Americans silently unpacked, washed, and then fell into bed until their dinner engagement.

As promised, Koserin met them in the lobby, escorting them to his waiting car.

Helen saw a young man sitting in their new employer's automobile. As the passenger stepped out, Koserin said, "Ladies, this bright young man is my son, and assistant manager, Max Jr."

Koserin beamed, clearly proud. "Max, these lovely young Americans are Helen Thompson and Lila Hart. They will be with us for some weeks."

Both girls smiled and shook the young man's hand. Helen quickly noticed that the son, though smaller in stature, with darker hair and glasses, shared the same temperament as his father—both men were smooth and amiable. Soon, the four were seated and enjoying dinner at an intimate club. Helen and Lila attempted to control their manners—it had been so long since breakfast, they could have eaten a horse.

Chatting pleasantly over coffee and liqueur, the manager, after a time inquired, "I presume both of you young ladies are prepared for tomorrow's early curtain?"

"Early, Mr. Koserin?" Helen said.

"Of course, my dear. The 6:30 dinner show." His easy smile slipped briefly, revealing a cool sternness. Helen froze, speechless, knowing their contract had stipulated two days of rest after their arrival.

"Of course we will be ready, but with the difficult day we just experienced I think we should get a good night sleep," Lila answered.

"Of course." Koserin replied. "And rest well, because the second show begins at 9:00 PM."

Helen wanted to remind Koserin about the terms of their contract, but something about the manager's expression intimidated her. "I will need to get together with the band in the morning and block out my act—and Lila, you?" Her friend nodded in agreement.

After another brief ride, they bade Mr. Koserin good evening, shook Max's hand, and returned to their room where Helen fell into bed, not moving until Lila's alarm buzzed at nine the next morning.

∗

Shaking off her grogginess, the dancer trudged over to the Copacabana, close to eleven in the morning. She towed Lila, still yawning behind her.

Pulling a brass handle on the double front doors, Helen and her friend stepped into an elegant vestibule. The pair maneuvered around knots of smartly dressed guests, and into the hotel's vast casino. To Helen it seemed as though acres of gambling tables filled the huge space. Oval baccarat tables, Black Jack islands, craps tables, and Roulette wheels, all covered the casino floor—morning gamblers sprinkled randomly around the nearly empty room, wagering stakes.

"Reminds me of Monte Carlo," Helen, impressed, mentioned. "I guess casinos are casinos."

"And there's nothing like the smell of stale alcohol and cigarettes first thing in the morning," Lila made a face. "I think I need a cup of coffee."

Wandering through the stylish lobby, the girls soon found Mr. Koserin. He was sitting among guests drinking black coffee at a table, reading his newspaper. He rose, broadly smiling, very pleased to see his new performers.

"No mention of your tribulations yesterday, not even a picture," he lightly remarked, gesturing at the paper. "I am very happy to see you. Come, ladies. Let me escort you to the stage and dressing facilities you will use. Then, perhaps enough time for you to rehearse."

As the three walked toward the showroom, Helen admired the interior's colonnaded Old World décor.

"The design in here is beautiful. It reminds me of Monte Carlo and Algiers" she complimented.

"My goodness, young lady. You have played in both locales?" Koserin remarked, impressed. "I am anxious to watch your performance this evening."

Helen suddenly felt her cheeks warming. She didn't like to sound pretentious. Luckily, the sounds of a piano floated down the corridor, ending the exchange. Moving through the entrance of the enormous showroom, she spied a dark-skinned pianist, seated on a low stage, idly warming up the keys.

Crossing the dance floor, Koserin called to the musician, "Sully, these are the girls I told you were coming—Miss Thompson and Miss Hart. Ladies, this is Sully."

"I'm Helen, and this is Lila," she smiled warmly, reaching over to shake Sully's hand.

"Well, who wants to go first? These keys are hot!" the friendly piano man flexed his knuckles.

Helen laughed with pleasure and relief, Sully was an American. Encouraged, she volunteered.

The dancer got right down to business, setting sheet music on the stand, and describing how her steps coordinated with the notes.

"This piece is up-tempo," the girl explained, leaning over the bench pointing to the notes. "It's called 'Black Coffee,' and I need some breaks here, and here. See where I penciled them in?"

Sully flexed his fingers again, and the two coordinated her steps to his tinkling of the keys.

"This jazz is steaming. You have anything else you're working on, Miss Helen?"

"Another syncopated number I need to run through." Helen responded, still a little winded. "And, I have another new piece called 'I Gotta Get Hot', but it's not ready, Sully. I haven't figured out the right arrangement or steps yet. I'll bring it around when I've ironed out the dance routine."

"Well, let's give this second piece a whirl," Sully suggested, turning back to the piano.

When they finished "Cinderella Brown," Helen said, "You've been great, thanks."

He smiled and charmingly saluted.

Walking back to their hotel with Lila, the girl finally overcame her travel fatigue thinking, *tonight should be fun.*

*

Glancing at the playbill, she checked again, making sure her act appeared third on the lineup,

"It's a good spot for a new act," she murmured, satisfied.

Wiggling into her costume, and stepping into her heels, Helen sensed a familiar rising charge of adrenaline hit her bloodstream. Quietly tiptoeing to the back side of the curtain, the dancer could easily hear the music. Waiting quietly, she realized the orchestra sounded off—somewhat flat. Peeking around the heavy satin drapery, her knees turned to jelly. No Sully in sight—a different piano man sat on the bench, and his playing sounded none too skillful.

"Where's my pianist?"

Horrified, her stomach turned. No one had mentioned any changes, and she felt completely helpless, as she had on the boat the day before. Suddenly, blaring horns startled her, signaling the next performance, as the audience charitably applauded the opening act.

Two dancers performed a soft shoe routine, bravely trying to keep time against the band's harsh din. All her earlier enthusiasm vanished as she tried to swallow down her constricted and dry throat. More polite clapping followed, and then she recognized her opening cue in the distorted thudding.

Spotting her sheet music on the piano, she knew the new bandleader planned to rely on her penciled notations. Too late to escape, the girl nervously walked to her position in the middle of the darkened stage, when a silent burst of concentrated pink light stunned her, saturating her sight. Blinking through negative vision, Helen acknowledged the faulty spotlights that had left her momentarily blinded.

Heart racing, she resorted to sound, listening for downbeats, relying on the band's musical direction. But the orchestra generated a poor interpretation of her arrangement—nowhere near faithful to her marked prompts. Continuing to blink the implosions from her vision, Helen opened her mouth to sing her first notes.

Black Coffee, I'm in trouble
Black Coffee, I see double...

The small melody in her own voice was overpowered by the sour horn section.

Concerned why her singing wasn't carrying, she glanced up to see the microphone, suspended too high to pick up her vocals. The stage manager had failed to lower it enough after the dancers. But Helen's act had begun, and she was forced to dig deep and mask all the technical problems.

Fortunately, her training and experience rescued the girl. She pushed her voice over the flat accompaniment, carrying the melody the musicians appeared unable to find. And despite the blinding beams washing out her vision, she executed her intricate routine, praying, *I hope my hands find the floor before my face.*

Finally, after what seemed never-ending, she again posed on her opening spot, forcing a smile, as the last dreary notes faded into silence.

The girl startled again, when the audience erupted into

unexpected applause—clearly not as critical, nor as aware, of the calamities she labored to hide. Looking out she thought, *either these people are too kind or are as blinded and deaf as me.*

The house lights flickered and began to rise, revealing the large, crowded ballroom as she gracefully curtsied, still blinking spots out of her eyes.

Three young men seated near the dance floor caught her eye, clearly American by their dress and relaxed posture. They all leaned forward over their drinks, elbows casually resting on the table, watching her, grinning. She couldn't seem to help smiling back at them, especially at the handsome blondish gentleman seated between the two others. He smiled back.

That was when she locked eyes with him—as he sat back, clapping. Without the blinding stage lights obscuring the room, Helen could see well enough to make out fair wavy hair, and a breathtaking, high-voltage smile. Helen was stunned—the band leader, light man, and stage manager all but forgotten.

*

Chum had carried on flirtations since arriving in Brazil, usually with the beautiful showgirls dancing at the casinos. But Frances, the girl at Roosevelt Field, was the only one who had captured his heart. Through their endless hours spent together in the hangar or soaring through the air, he had fallen in love with a married woman.

But this new girl, this sparking, compelling blonde on the stage, radiated a magnetism that surprised him. Closely studying her graceful bow, Chum became completely distracted by her fluid movements. Somewhere in his mind the thought registered, *I could watch her forever.*

Turning to Steve he eagerly asked, "Should I ask her over to the table?"

Steve laughed, entertained by Chum's obvious infatuation.

The pilot didn't notice.

"I wonder how long her contract runs," he murmured to no one.

*

Back in her dressing room Helen hastily tried to coil off her sequined leotard. Toweling sweat from her neck and forehead, she splashed water on her face, wiping off stage make-up. A sudden knock interrupted her thoughts. Throwing open her battered door, Helen faced a young man who held out a folded cocktail napkin. Nodding thanks to the silent courier, her hands fumbled, unfolding the flimsy tissue.

In English, written in a neat, careful hand she read, "My Dear Miss Thompson, You are a wonderful dancer, the best I've seen at the Copa. Would you join my table for a drink? Best, M.J. 'Chum' Chumbley."

The messenger loitered at the door, apparently hoping for a tip.

"Which gentleman sent this? Do you speak English?" Helen prodded. The busboy simply blinked. "I guess you don't," she said, handing him a coin.

Backstage notes were common enough, and though the girl had become rather astute on culling out the duds, she prayed this one was from the golden boy seated by the floor. Rereading "Chum," she felt fairly certain that had to be an American nickname.

Well, I'll never know hiding back here, she resolved, taking a last, appraising glance in the mirror.

Peeking around the rough silvery curtain again, Helen sighted the handsome man chatting with his friends. And the girl liked what she saw. He wore a light summer suit, and even seated, he seemed rather tall and rugged—a broad-shouldered man with a full, happy smile that flashed easily. His hair color, in the showroom's dim light, looked blonde and thick, with waves over his forehead bleached by the Rio sun. His eyes were very light, she decided from a distance, possibly blue or green. And she anxiously wanted to see closer.

Taking her second brave breath of the evening, Helen stepped out of her hiding place. Relief washed over her when the young man caught sight of her, and, half-standing over his table, motioned

Helen to come sit with him.

Hot damn, she rejoiced silently. *He is the "Chum" in the note.*

PURE ICE BLUE

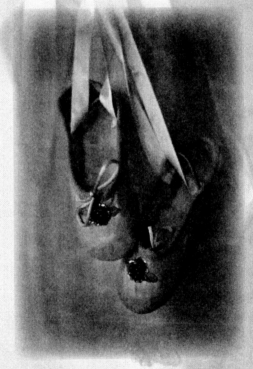

Rio de Janeiro
1936

While the attractive young man held a chair out for the lovely newcomer, his roommates, thoroughly entertained, scooted their chairs over to make room for her.

Chum proudly announced, "I'm Mont Chumbley," then more shyly added "but you can call me Chum, that's what everyone calls me."

The girl watched his mouth and eyes as he spoke.

"This is Paul Youngs, he shares our apartment," Chum casually gestured to his friend, "and Steve Bancroft— he lives there, too," the pilot added, very aware of Helen's proximity as she squeezed her chair closely into the tight space. She beamed her smile again at each roommate. And though they knew her name from the playbill, the girl politely introduced herself, "I'm Helen. Helen Thompson."

Now she felt unaccountably bashful speaking to this compelling young man, directly off her left shoulder.

"Enjoyed your performance. You sure can dance," Chum added awkwardly.

"Well, thank you. Rehearsal actually went smoother," she responded, recalling her annoyance.

"Not really sure how that could be. Haven't seen such a good performance since I started coming to the club," Chum said with a smile. Helen noticed a nuance in Chum's voice when he spoke that she couldn't place, giving her a chance to reverse the subject to him.

"I can't place your accent, where is your home?" she asked.

Chum laughed. "I was born and raised in southwestern Virginia, Pulaski County, where my family still lives—they farm," he added.

Helen again looked into his eyes, and they were blue, pure ice blue, bluer than hers, Helen noted, and grew embarrassed recognizing her impolite staring. The young man seemed not to mind at all, as he too studied her face.

She laughed. "You don't look too much like a farmer."

Chuckling with her he added, "Milked cows, plowed fields, fed chickens, the whole kit and caboodle." Both of Chum's companions appeared to be amused by their buddy's oblivious absorption. Finally Steve asked, "Helen, what would you like to drink?"

"Bourbon on the rocks, please."

"And another beer here if you're buying, Bancroft," Chum added.

"Are all of you from Virginia?" Helen politely probed, glancing at the other two men.

"Hell, no!" Steve gasped. "I come from God's Country. The San Joaquin Valley in California."

Chum butted in, "And you, Helen, where's home?"

Steve and Paul looked at each other and shrugged in resignation. Evidently they were only permitted to watch this conversation.

"My sister and I were both born in Chicago, but we grew up in New York—Jamaica Heights, in Queens."

Chum at once pressed her for more information. How long was her engagement in the lounge? Did she like Rio? How long had she been in town?

Helen reflected a moment and then honestly answered, "I haven't been here long enough to finish unpacking. I've seen nothing but the port and a dinner club last night."

"Oh, well, okay" Chum faltered. A look at his amused roommates caught him short. *Too eager, too eager,* he chided himself.

Unaware of Chum's fumble, the girl continued, "My cabin mate and I did get up at dawn yesterday morning. We wanted to see the sun rising over the city and the bay from the ship. It was very beautiful." Helen found herself peeking again into those metallic blue eyes.

Chum smiled.

"Well, you haven't seen much, yet. Would you like to go with me?" he paused, "if you aren't too busy"

This boy was so handsome, so polite, and so pleasant to be with, that she didn't hesitate,

"That would be nice," Helen brightly consented. Her face then clouded "But I don't know exactly when I can get away. I need to work a little with the orchestra tomorrow." She frowned again, recalling her performance.

Beaming a wide irresistible smile, Chum assured her, "I promise to keep the date open. I can wait, and we will go when you have time."

At that, it occurred to Helen she didn't know why he was in Rio, how he could so easily get away from his job.

"What is it you do here, Chum?"

Clearing his throat he explained, "I sell airplanes. I work for an American manufacturer, Waco Aircraft. Their factory is back in the states, in Ohio. It's my job to show our models, demonstrate the planes, fly the big brass around, and then, hopefully make sales to the Brazilian Air Ministry."

Helen's doubtful face gave her away.

"Never flown in a plane, Helen?" he asked.

She laughed, "Shows that much? No, never. But I'd love to give flying a whirl."

All too soon, Lila walked up to the table nodding to each man and still looking rather weary. She heaved a sigh, "Helen, if you're ready we can leave."

Helen hesitated, hating to end the evening so early, but feeling her two long days as well. "I suppose we should. I need to get back here in the morning pretty early."

Chum piped up, "You're not staying here? Where's your hotel?"

"The manager gave us an option, but the Copa is too expensive. The Bandeirantes is more reasonable." Helen merely pointed in the general direction where their hotel faced the boulevard, a building two blocks up.

"I'd be glad to walk you back, make sure you get home."

The dancer smiled. "Thank you, I would like that."

Paul and Steve downed the rest of their drinks, Paul adding, "We'll tag along. Early morning for me too. And Steve, well, he'll just lose his shirt at the roulette table if he stays."

Steve shrugged his shoulders.

A light breeze cooled the moist air, making the perfect night for a stroll. Chum walked next to Helen, saying little. Approaching the hotel's entryway, he murmured, "Have a good rest, Helen."

The girl floated upstairs to her room. Lila heavily trudged behind.

*

Helen rolled, stretching in her bed. Gathering her bearings, she glanced over to the other bed, where Lila was still asleep.

"Chum," she whispered as she recalled the previous night. "The music at the club, ugh," intruded into her reverie, taking priority. "Wake up, Lila," Helen croaked, "We need to rehearse."

Following a quick breakfast the girls pulled open the grand doors again, finding Mr. Koserin reading his newspaper and drinking his thick black coffee. Helen was determined to vent her dissatisfaction over the foul-ups of the previous night. But no matter how hard she worked herself up, all that came out of her mouth was "Morning. That microphone…"

"Already fixed," Koserin interrupted, more interested in his reading.

"Oh, all right, then," Helen mumbled. Unable to say anything else, she escaped to the showroom to rehearse, chiding, *I am such a coward; where's Bertha when I need her?*

That evening, Chum did come back. As Helen found her mark on the shadowy stage, a softer spotlight cast a halo around her as she danced both shows. Each time the house lights rose, there he waited, cigar smoldering in an ashtray, nursing a glass of beer. Taking her final bow, she looked over, signaling with her index finger to give her a minute to change.

Chum nodded with a wink.

Dressed in a black satin cocktail dress, the dancer drew up to his table. Chum sat alone.

"Where are the boys this evening?" Helen asked looking around.

"Steve's flying and Paul had a date. You miss them?" he teased.

Helen blushed.

Smiling, Chum handed her a Rio newspaper, "I found a review of the act."

Helen became concerned, expecting the worst.

"Don't look so worried," he laughed. "The critic described your performance as 'devilish.'"

With that comment, Chum wore a devilish grin. "Read it, it's good," he encouraged.

Helen scanned the column, secretly pleased that she got away with improvising through that disastrous opening night.

"So what about our sightseeing date?" he asked, drawing her back from the review. "If you could find some time, maybe we could drive and picnic on the top of one the foothills above the city tomorrow."

"I'd like that, Chum," she quickly agreed. He beamed in return. Looking into his eyes she no longer could hear anything beyond her heart beating in her ears. Trivial concerns such as sabotaged performances, money for her mother, or insistent old boyfriends vanished.

He stared back silently, caught as well, in the power of the moment. Finally Chum cleared his throat, twice, saying "How does 3:00 tomorrow afternoon sound?"

*

The two meandered along the beach hand in hand as Chum escorted Helen home from the casino. Helen felt a contentment she had never known as the two reached the canopied entrance to her hotel.

Chum gently pulled the girl into his arms.

"Come here" he said with a sigh.

She exhaled, too surprised and relaxed to envision any other ending to the evening.

They embraced for more than a moment then Chum smiled brilliantly, whispering, "Get a good night's sleep. We have a big date tomorrow."

Balancing against a column and struggling to slow her breathing, Helen finally arrived into her room and slumped down onto her bed. Lila hadn't come back from the casino yet so Helen was free to think.

A handsome, nice, and well situated American boy seems to like me, and all I had to do is travel to another hemisphere to meet him! She mused as she giggled euphorically. *I have four weeks here for sure, four more with my option. But I'm not sure eight weeks is enough.*

Replaying his embrace over and over in her mind, Helen recognized, *my heart is still thumping. I feel like I've turned fifty spotters but this is much, much nicer.*

She lay back, in a futile attempt to calm her body down. Eventually, rolling to her side Helen glanced at her night table.

Two letters leaned against the lamp.

Lila must have brought them up, she guessed.

Picking them up, she saw the first came from her mother and the other, nearly covered in a checkerboard of British postage stamps, bore Elie's distinctive script.

"Oh dear," she sighed, heavily. Helen opened and scanned each letter in turn. Bertha, of course, was miserable and lonesome, and Elie chided, *why have you been so elusive in keeping me informed of your situation?*

Cold reality extinguished her joy. One moment she felt stirring fascination, the next—nagging remorse and guilt. Helen had been neglecting her mother, and was again saddled with the problem of Elie.

With a dutiful-driven urgency, Helen felt compelled to right things as quickly as she could.

Focusing on her mother first, she tore into her steamer trunk, found her airmail stationary, and began a cheerful, chatty letter home. She described the fiasco on the docks, then the nearly disastrous opening night.

Understanding what placated her mother most, Helen promised a $100 check on her payday. She finished up the letter by consoling Bertha, writing that there was a possibility she could be done in Rio in four weeks.

Rereading her quick note she told herself, *I pray that I stay here, but Bert wouldn't understand; she'd say that I'm selfish.*

"And, Elie, what am I going to do about you?" Helen mumbled, stumped. Reading his letter more closely, she struggled to find a sunny response:

> *My Darling Helen,*
> *That you sailed to Brazil with no word has added to my perplexity. If you would consider my proposal, your need to perform would no longer be necessary. I can look after you, and your mother. Please write to me and tell me your thoughts. Consider extending a bit of kindness to the one who cherishes you.*
>
> > *My Eternal Devotion,*
> > *Elie*

She now knew, for a fact, Elie wasn't the one she wanted. After two evenings spent with Chum, the girl was clear on that point.

Exhaling, she attempted a cordial response, trying to convey with her pen that her feelings were of friendship, and did not extend to fiancée or bride.

Purposefully, Helen's tone remained distant, polite, and informative. She described the casino, her contract, and what a wonderful opportunity she had found. How she couldn't pass up such a chance for her career—that would have been foolish, and on and on.

For just an instant she considered throwing her response in the trash. But she didn't.

"I don't quite know what to say, or what to do about you, Elie," Helen whispered, sealing another bland letter.

A HORA
DA PARTIDA

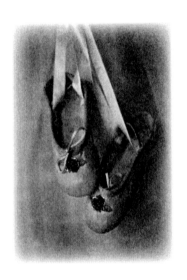 

The Hour of Our Parting
Rio de Janeiro
1936

After that first night, the two were regularly seen together. Chum picked Helen up from the club each night, his attention thrilling Helen, rather than putting her off. From the stage she could always find him in the crowd, silhouetted in the entrance, against the backlight of the casino. Chum casually leaned his shoulder against the entry, crossed his arms taking in her act.

She grew giddy in the dressing room anticipating her walk home with him. Taking his strong arm for the dreamlike stroll along the beach to her hotel—his heartfelt, powerful affection at the door.

As for Chum, he found a gratification in Helen's company that he had never before known.

They talked for hours about their lives, their hopes, and many of their earlier adventures. More soothing was the time spent together saying nothing, just holding hands in quiet solitude. She knew she wanted to do anything Chum was interested in, just glad to spend what short time she had with him.

"Hop in, Helen, I've got some great stops planned," Chum promised with a grin. He had an automobile owned by Waco, and was delighted to chauffeur his new girl around the city. Royal palms, evenly positioned, shaded the wide boulevard as they motored past. Helen leaned back in her seat watching the water on one side and the rising mountains on the other. As her mind wandered she turned her attention from the view to her new beau.

"Tell me about your family, Chum. You know, I still can't picture you in overalls, holding a pitchfork."

The vista from the car stretched in scope, as more sea and sky unfolded, winding up the steep terrain. Chum glanced over at her thoughtfully for a moment before he replied.

"My father's people have lived on the same land for generations," he began. "My mother's family moved to the valley later. Mother's sister, my aunt, came there too, with her family."

Thinking a minute he continued, "I spent a lot of time with my aunt and uncle growing up." Helen noticed his change of tone.

"So you didn't stay at home much?"

"I liked town better," Chum answered. "And you, Helen, your family?"

"Not so much to tell, it's just my mother, sister and me—we're very close. We have a little apartment on 45th Street near Times Square. My father's been gone a long time." She grew quiet.

"I'm sorry for your loss," Chum kindly replied. "But that's enough of the serious. Let's explore paradise, shall we?" His eyes shined.

For the next few hours the young couple roamed the city, following routes to picturesque outlying areas. Later in the day Chum's sedan purred up to Sugarloaf Mountain, on the peninsula above Guanabara Bay.

Sitting on the broad hood of the automobile, the couple settled closely together on the warm dark metal, sharing supper. Helen smiled often, as Chum told her stories of flying, Virginia manure, and Rio, while pointing out the scenic landmarks on all sides of their vantage point. From that glorious afternoon, the two became inseparable. If not at the field, Chum lunched with the girl, and Helen began to hurry through rehearsals to meet him for an early dinner.

And each night, after the show, he took her hand for the enchanted walk home.

Chum took time to introduce the girl to a variety of decidedly male pastimes. Helen attended her first horse race cheering with him in the roaring stands.

"In England I just listened to the races on the radio, and the difference is spectacular. Thanks for bringing me, it's much better seeing it," she remarked.

Chum, on another evening, accompanied Helen to the fights—also a first time experience for her.

"This may sound strange, but I like boxing a lot, too," she confessed.

His eyes twinkled with pleasure. "I think it's the company." he ribbed.

And though she quite enjoyed most of her time shepherded around by Chum, she couldn't ignore the appalling poverty she witnessed from the car window. All around the bay the palatial homes of the wealthy contrasted cruelly with the squalor only a stone's throw away.

Chum noticed her staring and explained, "Those rows of shacks are called favelas. The poor make them from anything they can find; tin, sheet metal, boards, and cardboard."

"It's a pity, she murmured, staring at the cluttered slopes above the city.

"Especially the ragged children," she added, as she watched a tiny girl scrounge through a trash pile beside a small dog.

Most of the couple's courtship flourished on the pristine beaches curving around the picturesque bay. For hours the two could be seen murmuring quietly on a blanket, playing games with their friends, or browning, side by side, on the beaches.

"Show her your stuff, Chum; up on those hands," Paul challenged him, laughing.

Stepping from her cabana where she had just changed into her bathing suit, Helen caught the tail end of Paul's challenge. Looking first to Chum, then over to Paul, Helen dropped her towel and bottle of suntan oil into the sand, dove into a full handstand herself, and headed straight to her beau, finally falling into his lap.

"You are really something," he whispered in her ear, kissing her cheek. Then, general challenges erupted from the crowd. Two lines of friends formed, and Helen and Chum raced on their hands, only to pile up laughing after only a few feet. Piggyback races with Chum carrying Helen on his shoulders gave other couples a chance to compete, rushing down the beach to a sandy finish line. The group tossed the medicine ball, vying to keep it in the air as long as possible under a storm of friendly taunts.

Late afternoon, the two detached from the group—again quietly whispering secret conversations on a blanket. As she looked into his eyes with wonder, Helen reflected, *this is incredible, and time is passing too quickly. This man is the most important thing in my life. What am I going to tell Bert and Eileen?*

Later that afternoon, before rehearsal, she penned a letter to New York. Buried among other cheery sentences, Helen inserted, "I've met a very nice American boy."

"That's all I better say for now," Helen decided, speaking out loud. "I have to take this slow with mother because this time, it matters. What if she tells me no—no boyfriends? Bert only needs to meet Chum, and then she'll understand how perfect he is for me."

Carefully rereading her letter, sensitive to what mattered most, she sweetened her vaguely revealing note with a healthy money order.

That evening, Chum waited for her inside the showroom—an evening that included a fierce stare-down with a Brazilian who tried to send a note of his own to the dancer. As they wandered back to the hotel above the beach on elaborately patterned sidewalks, Helen carefully mentioned her note to New York.

"I mentioned your name in a letter home today," she began. The girl gauged his reaction closely after this awkward admission. Chum surprised her.

"You posting it at the hotel?" he asked.

"Yes, it's going out on the next Munson," she answered confused.

"I can send them by air with Steve or Paul, you know."

"Oh, oh right." He didn't bat an eye at her confession. Feeling strangely reassured, Helen remembered his roommates were Pan American pilots, one or the other usually flying to Miami or New York many times a month. And after that night, Helen's mail, with the exception of Elie's letter, flew to New York, compliments of her new sweetheart. Chum made sure that her mail rode with his friends on the flight deck, safe and sound.

Brightly, Helen used her best, "isn't that nice," tone to mention Chum's name again in another letter to her mother. She praised her new love for his consideration, and for moving her letters much faster to New York.

A CONTRAST

Rio de Janeiro
1936

Rain poured down outside the Copacabana when Carmen Morales quietly tiptoed in, closing her dripping umbrella, up from Buenos Aires.

"Carmen!" Helen called out during rehearsal, recognizing her from the stage. "What a surprise! It's been too long!" She rushed to hug her friend.

"I've missed you so much, Helen," Carmen responded, sounding a little drained.

"Well, your timing is swell; we just finished. Are you hungry? Would you like some coffee, Carmen? Did your ship just arrive?"

"Yes, but just the coffee," Carmen sadly smiled for a moment. Helen found cups and poured coffee, and then the two sat in the lounge, at a quiet table away from the noisy showroom.

"Glad you're here, sweetie, but why no word? What's going on down south with the kids?"

Carmen took in a sharp breath. "Earl's still dancing in a show, but everyone else wants out of their contracts. We—the girls and I—are booked in some seedy dives. All in all, pretty discouraging."

"Is that all, Carmen? You seem so low. Is it the nightclub?" Suddenly, she realized the missing piece. "Earl—he's not here. Didn't he travel with you?"

Carmen dissolved into tears. She took a breath, steadied herself then blurted out, "Earl and his new dance partner are having an affair and everyone knows. I'm so humiliated, and I can't seem to pull myself together."

Helen squeezed Carmen's hand. Her friend pulled out a handkerchief with her free hand, dabbing her eyes and nose. In a strained voice, Carmen continued, "I'm seriously looking at returning to New York. Earl's show returns to Paris soon, and he's said nothing about my going with him. He doesn't care, not at all. I'm devastated, Helen. I thought I knew him."

Helen froze. She remembered how smitten Earl had been. He showed such devotion to Carmen in Europe that it was hard to imagine he would ever stray. Helen simply couldn't picture it.

"We were all taken in, Carmen. Earl duped us, too. And I am so sorry. Is there anything I can do to help?"

"No, kid. Just thanks for letting me impose on you unannounced…"

"Impose on me? You, my dear, dear friend are nowhere near imposing. I'm glad you're here."

Though unintentionally, Carmen had added more to Helen's doubts.

"I plan on going to Buenos Aires. It's the only way to stay down here," she told Lila later. "But after Carmen's description of the working conditions—well, it's a worry. And Carmen, poor Carmen! I hurt for her, but I'm still so elated about my Chum. What a contrast—both of us on opposite ends of love, trying to talk."

Despite her valid fear of a bad booking in Argentina, she knew she had no choice. Helen reassured herself, silently, *I have to go; it's the only way to stretch out my stay and handle mother. When the Rio contract runs out, I can't just jump a ship home.*

*

Chum struggled with the same dilemma. Talking to his friend he complained, "If she stayed here, I could take care of her, Steve. She doesn't need to go to Buenos Aires or even work here in Rio. But she seems worried about offending her mother if she can't justify staying."

"You two will work it out, buddy. That girl is as head over heels as you are," his friend assured him.

"Thanks, Steve. I really hate to see her leave."

"You've got it bad, you poor bastard," Bancroft chortled.

"You're a knucklehead, California boy," Chum chided in return.

*

Each night Chum lingered in the casino, playing a little roulette, or black jack, making sure Helen was safe inside and that no drunk was getting too friendly.

Walking later on the beach, Chum lightly explained, "There are a lot of big bad wolves out there, Miss Red Ridinghood."

Helen tsk'd at his over-protective silliness, but was flattered. Many nights he walked Helen directly into the lift at the hotel. If empty, which was usually the case, that little moving space allotted brief moments of private heat.

Chum, barely controlled, whispered, "Move in with me; this is not enough."

"Move in with you?" She stepped back.

"Helen," he firmly replied, "What we have found together can't be measured by time."

After a couple of days, while lying on the beach, warm sun heating their shoulders and legs, Helen had made her decision. Leaning over, her chin on his shoulder, she whispered, "Do you think you might have room for a steamer trunk in that apartment?"

"I'll knock out a wall and remodel," Chum breathed in reply.

*

"Chum—honey, would you come into the showroom tonight? I've worked up a new number and I need your opinion," Helen asked her love as she headed out the door for rehearsal.

Reaching for her hand as she traipsed by, Chum replied, "Glad to, honeybunch. Probably save me from losing twenty bucks or more at the roulette table."

At the 9:30 PM show, Helen took her mark oh center stage. In the darkness Chum, also feeling her butterflies, sat close to the floor. An improving orchestra hit the opening chord, the drummer tapped a syncopated beat, and then the spot light illumined the beautiful dancer. Chum watched transfixed, mesmerized, again, by her swaying and lithe response to the music:

In Duluth I sang in the choir
Full of youth and a burning desire
I came here to be an opera singer
Now look at me
A torso slinger.

The piece was a hit. The applause, appreciative and enthusiastic, left the dancer smiling. Helen later told Chum the title, "I Gotta Get Hot."

"Well, I liked it," he chuckled, thinking again of the words and her brassy choreography. "Honestly, honey you were great, and funny, and gorgeous, and talented..."

She hopped up and kissed her delighted beau's smiling mouth. They both chuckled.

After Helen's last bow, the two walked into the quiet apartment. Steve's bedroom door hung open, the room dark. Paul's door shut tight, his hearty snoring resonating through the wall.

"How does he sleep making all that racket?" Helen giggled quietly.

"Sounds like a sawmill," Chum agreed.

Lying quietly in the dark, as a cool breeze ruffled the sheers from the open window, Chum asked her, "Is it necessary to dress in such skimpy costumes?"

Helen, surprised by his tone, asked, "What's wrong, Chum?"

"Well, Helen, you know those flips and walkovers; it just doesn't seem right to wear so little doing them."

"Oh, Chum, sweetheart, that's just show business. My approach to dance, my trademark is acrobatic in style. My hands are as important as my feet. I couldn't perform those moves dressed in long or heavy clothes."

Chum wasn't appeased. "I don't like other men leering at you; it just doesn't sit well with me." Both lay quiet a moment as he lightened his tone mentioning, "I sure like that cute ABC number you sing..."

"Rhythm in My Nursery Rhymes?" Helen asked.

"Yeah, that one. Your dance has a good tempo…"

"And I'm covered up in a full length evening gown," she squeezed his hand, sympathetically.

"It is an attractive, full length evening gown," he teased.

"Oh, Chum, as long as you're around, I am not worried about those wolves."

He shook his head at her naivety, "You are such a sweet girl, and I know you've worked hard. You're not as good as you are by chance; your dedication is admirable. It's just performing in front of strangers night after night. I want you with me."

*

Unloading his anxiety to Steve, just returned from a flight, Chum fretted, "Helen is so innocent—so trusting, she thinks since she has been safe so far, no one is a threat."

"It's hard not to feel a little territorial. Helen is a sweet-natured and beautiful girl. But, Chum, I wouldn't worry too much. Having Helen is probably worth the anxiety," Steve assured him. "And don't forget, bud, she's just as crazy about you."

Chum's face wore a troubled expression, and Steve couldn't help but laugh. "Look pal, I'll keep an eye on her when you have to fly out, how's that? You worry too much, Chum; it's going to make you gray."

Attempting a weak grin, Chum replied, "Thanks."

"You really got it bad, buster," the roommate muttered, shaking his head.

*

Continuing her campaign to ease her new boyfriend into her letters, Helen wrote a rather ordinary note home, this time only mentioning Chum toward the end.

*Chum is still so nice. You will meet him—he's coming
back to New York with me when this show ends.*

She pursed her lips while scanning over her letter's contents.
"That should answer some of the questions Mother must have."

Aside from Chum's endorsement, Helen had other tricky
business to add in her letter.

"I'm singing more now, and am wardrobed in lovely evening
gowns each night," she began. Carefully selecting her next words,
she described her musical numbers, and the colors of her various
costumes, then came to her point.

"Mr. Koserin didn't know that I trained in ballet and asked me
to work some into my performance. And the best news, Mother,
Mr. Koserin announced that he was exercising his option for four
more weeks! Isn't that marvelous?"

Predicting her mother's certain displeasure at the news Helen
inserted a check for $175, adding, "... *and more soon, now that I am
staying on. Love You, Helen.*"

The girl sighed leaning back in her chair, muttering aloud, "I
wish I could come clean and tell her everything."

Left out was the fact she was living at Chum's apartment and
only saw Lila at the club.

As the dancer relished her contract extension at the Copa, she
continued to wonder about the future, the Argentine job. As late as
July, she still hadn't heard whether she was going south to Buenos
Aires, as she hoped, or home to the States. The thought of leaving
the setting of so much happiness prompted a painful dread.

*Without Chum in New York, I will go out of my mind sitting around that
apartment,* she thought.

At dinner, the two attempted to work out some possible solutions
to their quandary.

"Sweetheart, you need to calm down. If Koserin doesn't offer
you a new contract in Argentina, we'll travel back to New York
together. I have three months of vacation I haven't used, and would
love to spend it with you in the city," he assured her, squeezing her

hand on the tabletop.

"Yes, of course, that would be wonderful," Helen responded doubtfully, casting down her troubled eyes. "But, Chum, my only other hope of staying longer is the Buenos Aires offer. If that worked out, we'd have four more weeks to see each other; Buenos Aires must be a relatively easy flight for you, right?"

Chum nodded. She continued, "Then later we could use your vacation time, which keeps us together longer."

After rehearsal the next day, Helen took her uncertainties to her boss. But, for the first time since they met, Mr. Koserin didn't have all the answers.

"I don't know if I can guarantee Buenos Aires for you, my dear. The clubs have not yet responded to any of my cables. I'm fairly certain that an agreement will materialize for you. But for now be patient. As soon as I know anything, I promise to immediately inform you."

So, the young lovers had no choice but to try and remain calm while waiting for word from Mr. Koserin. It was a restless time, not knowing the future, painfully in love, and agonizing over any separation that they knew had to come.

*

Amid Helen's troubles and anxieties, a disconcerting letter arrived, postmarked Piccadilly, London. Lila delivered the note to her during an afternoon rehearsal.

Just taking the envelope from her friend weighed her down with guilt and blame. Staring at the correspondence, which she had placed on a music stand, finally got the better of her. Departing from the casino, she opened the letter in dread, took a deep breath, and read the following:

> *I presume that by the time this letter reaches you— you*
> *will have done most of the eight weeks with attendant success,*
> *I hope, and the casino will be exercising their option. Your*

Mother did not tell me much about the company or act you went with. If it is not asking much you might drop me a line, by air-mail as this letter, addressed to No. 141, New Bond Street c/o The Polyfoto International Company Lt, mark the envelope "Personal."

"Well, not as bad as I expected," she managed to say, her throat constricting. Then tears unexpectedly burned her eyes and began to spill over.

"I just can't do the right thing by Elie!" She choked, her voice breaking. "I feel so horrible, now that I understand what it means to love someone."

Helen's tears fell profusely, a mix of guilt over breaking a heart, her passionate love for Chum, and a daughter's obligation to her mother. Dragging her feet back to the apartment, she stretched out on the bed while her tears traced down her temples and into her hair. Lying still for a quarter of an hour, her weeping slowed, replaced with a sudden insight.

Elie's still in London. He hasn't left for his grand tour. She picked up his letter again.

"Delay stemmed from political upheavals in Spain," the girl read aloud. *That terrible civil war in Spain, who are they, again?* She searched her memory to recall. *Fascists against loyalists? That's right, and Hitler has something to do with it. No wonder Elie is still stuck in London. I've seen those newsreels screened at the theater; so awful, Chum said we didn't need the English subtitles.*

She tucked the Belgian's letter away with the rest of his past correspondence, wondering why she kept so much of Elie.

Helen lay back again, sadly thinking of the kind Belgian—then of beautiful, wonderful Chum, still working out at the field. Her heart swelled with affection.

My Elie days belong in the past, the girl firmly resolved.

*

"Good news, my dear," he greeted Helen across the nearly empty casino lounge. Jolly as ever, Mr. Koserin announced, "I have heard from Buenos Aires." He waved a telegram in his hand. "You had nothing to worry about, your contract finally came through."

Filled with joy and relief, Helen placed her hands over her mouth, and her eyes sparkled. Clearly enjoying her reaction, Koserin explained, "You're to play the Don Dean Club, a very exclusive venue, very chic. The perfect setting for a perfect dancer."

"Thank you, but I don't know that club, Mr. Koserin."

"Oh, Helen, Don Dean's name means sophistication and prestige," he explained. "And it's famous for its stellar quality of entertainment."

"Oh, goodness! Are you sure I'm booked there?"

Koserin nodded, "Absolutely. This is fortunate for you. And your performances will be wonderful. I told them as much in a glowing endorsement. Oh, and one more thing; Dean is an American band leader. That should make you very happy."

"Thank you so much for your assistance in this, Mr. Koserin. This contract means a lot to me." She struggled for words, finally settling on, "You have been a great boss."

"Might your gratitude have something to do with a certain young pilot?" He smiled, paternally.

Helen, a little embarrassed, dodged the subject, "My friends playing in Buenos Aires have not been as lucky. You've made that difference for me and I am grateful."

Later came the part she dreaded—breaking the news to her mother. Bertha had been impatient to have Helen come home, and again, the girl worded her new letter with care.

> *Dearest Mother,*
> *I hope this letter finds you well and not too lonely. Is sis home? I haven't heard any news.*
> *My option to play in Buenos Aires has come through. Mother, what an opportunity! The venue is called The Don*

Dean Club, and plays host to a very exclusive clientele.

Mr. Koserin described the club as the destination in Buenos Aires, for the wealthy, government officials and Europeans visiting the city. What a chance to showcase my work!

So I guess that I'll be a bit longer getting home, but I know that you understand the importance of seizing opportunities. The contract negotiated gives me two weeks of guaranteed performances, $55.00 a week in American currency and an extension if the Club exercises their option. The best part, Mother, I am the headliner! And even better than that, I've been billed as a singer."

The girl knew Bertha had always dreamed of Helen as a sultry chanteuse, and would probably not grumble too much. Carefully, Helen completed her letter by dropping in her old friend's name, rather than Chum's. She then added a persuasive spin by downplaying the extended stay.

Carmen is there and can especially help me get acquainted with the city. You know she has been in Buenos Aires for quite a while, now. She says that this club is top notch too. With the available ships coming and going twice a month, I would have to wait for the next Munson liner heading north, anyway. I figured that I might as well work and make a little more money.

Sweetening her news, Helen added in a final reassurance:

I decided to send you another check so that you don't have to scrimp. I already have my steamship ticket for home so that expense can't hold me up in any way.

> *Love,*
> *Helen*

*

The young couple, neither able to sleep, tangled together on his bed, murmured quietly as his roommates slept. Chum eventually got up, opened his bureau, and handed a large envelope to his weepy girl.

"I want you to take this so you don't forget me," he whispered. She slowly pulled a large photo out, glimpsing first his cocky smile, then a full casual pose in front of his Waco. In the lower corner of the glossy he had penned,

To Helen, with my very best wishes always,
Love Chum, Rio '36.

Laughing through her tears Helen huskily quipped, "You look so happy here. Is it due to my arrival or departure?"

Holding her close, he teased, "It's the last one I have. I sent the rest to my mother."

They both chuckled quietly, and then she began weeping again.

Clutching her handkerchief, Helen reached over the side of the bed into her purse.

"I want you to remember me, too." She blotted her eyes while giving him a black and white portrait. "He gazed at her photo— Helen flirtatious, smiling at an attractive angle, wearing a broad brimmed hat. Then he read, *"Chum, you will always have my best wishes, and my Love, Sincerely, Helen."*

"We sound like affectionate pen pals," Helen laughed, while fresh tears trickled down her cheeks. They fell silent. Finally, Chum spoke, coaxing, "Come back in, sweetheart," And Helen folded herself back into his arms until the sun rose.

BUZZING THE TRAIN

Buenos Aires
1936

"It's only two weeks, love," the dancer reminded Chum, lingering before she boarded her train.

"Rio will feel empty with you gone," Chum exhaled uneasily. "I will fly down as soon as I can, and will spend as much time as possible with you, until you're through down there. Both Steve and Paul have promised to check on you during their flights south. And, it won't bother me if you wanted to call at any time. Please, please be careful, darling." Holding both of her shoulders, gazing intently into her extraordinary sky-blue eyes, Chum reiterated, "I'm serious, Helen, if you need anything, *anything*, write, cable, or call—don't hesitate."

Chum suddenly knew at that moment, with his eyes fixed on her exquisite face that the Don Dean Club would not get their two week extension — Helen wouldn't be available after her contract expired. He kept this epiphany to himself.

The distressed dancer, not as confident about his devotion, sadly bid her new love goodbye, halfheartedly plodding aboard the train for Argentina.

She found a berth facing a woman and her child. Unable to generate a polite smile, she looked out the window. Chum stood below on the platform wearing the same gloomy expression.

Throwing aside her decorum, Helen passionately placed her right hand onto the window. He responded to her gesture with a sad smile, and raised his palm on the opposite side. They both continued to press the window, even after the train shuttered forward. Chum jogged a few steps, gradually pacing to a stop. Helen dissolved into grief. The lady in the opposite seat quickly produced some chocolates and oranges, distracting her gawking son with the snack.

After nearly two hours of bumpy travel, a puffy-eyed Helen was abruptly jolted awake. She looked around, momentarily disoriented. Then she and the other riders detected a distinct whining, mechanical hum rising above the din of the train's thundering locomotive.

Alarm spread, passengers in the car raising a panicked chatter. Shouting at once, the group moved chaotically about the train car, most rushing to the windows. At the same time a porter burst into the car, scurrying down the aisle, shouting in both Spanish and English, "Please return to your seats. All is well; nothing is awry with the equipment. Please calm yourselves and quickly sit down!"

Frightened, Helen searched out her own window looking for smoke or worse, fire streaking past the glass. Instead, a deep sense of wonder spread through her being, replacing any fear of danger. She caught sight of a lone Waco Cabin biplane soaring above the trees and power lines parallel to the speeding train. Both of her hands now caressed the window, as an enchanted smile lit her surprised face. Then, as though he knew she was watching, the pilot waggled his wings in hello, soon pulling up, gaining altitude, and the little plane then looped back toward Rio. Helen, her heart full, sat back, marveling at the power of her cascading emotions.

*

"I can see my name!" the dancer rejoiced. Displayed in the center of the club's marquee was *American Helen Thompson*, visible from a half block away. A man who turned out to be the club manager greeted her at the entry, "Welcome, welcome Miss Thompson. I am very glad to meet you."

Helen replied, "Very nice to meet you, too…?"

"Oh, oh, Oscar Fuentes; I manage this club. You are here to, perhaps, rehearse?"

"I am, Mr. Fuentes. I have my sheet music and hoped to practice," she responded almost as a question.

"Certainly, please come into the showroom, the musicians are collecting as we speak."

With whispering footfalls, they walked across the carpeted lobby, soon transitioning to clipped steps on polished parquet announcing the two as they passed into the lounge. Helen listened to a cacophony of sounds as the band warmed up instruments.

"You need not worry about the patrons—no mixing with the crowd is required. Our orchestra is quite accomplished and we are looking forward to your performance."

She relaxed over his words, thinking, *so far so good. I am appearing at the top of the bill. Old Mistinguett friends are nearby, and if I have to be away from Chum, that makes time here tolerable. Plus I get to roll over some vocals.*

"Good morning, Oscar. Who is your lovely friend?"

Helen smiled, recognizing her new boss from his picture in the lobby.

"Mr. Dean, this is Miss Thompson from New York via Rio de Janeiro." Helen extended her hand.

"Hello, I'm Don Dean, Los Angeles via Bogota."

Both Americans laughed in a fraternal way.

"Fellas, this is Helen. Say hello!" dark-haired Dean instructed his band.

"Hello, Helen" they all shouted in unison as she shyly waved.

"I'll leave you now, my dear. You are in good hands," Oscar announced. "It was lovely meeting you."

Helen turned back to the bandleader as he prompted, "Let's get to work, Miss America!"

"Yes, sir. These are my numbers, and I have only practiced them, not performed them. My opener, 'Goody Goody,' is a bit up tempo and I thought it would be a place to start," she thumbed the sheet music open.

"Good; the band knows this one, Helen," answered Dean, looking over the arrangement.

Helen handed the leader another score, "You Are My Lucky Star."

"It's a little jazzy…"

"Great song. Yes, we can work this out. And you're still holding...?"

"It's a little slower— a ballad, "First You Have Me High, Then You Have Me Low," the girl answered, handing over her last score. The musicians began sight-reading copies of "Goody Goody," tooting lightly on horns, tinkling on the piano, and strumming a guitar, as they worked out the details of her arrangement. Helen continued to discuss some points with Dean explaining, "I've been billed as a singer, but my first love is dancing." What would you think of bridging the music in spots to allow some dance steps?"

"Absolutely; the audience should appreciate the surprise. I didn't realize you were so versatile, Miss Thompson."

"Helen, please."

"Call me Don, then," the bandleader encouraged.

Days after Helen's solid opening, Dean pitched a proposition for Helen that he posed just as she arrived for rehearsal.

"Afternoon, Helen," Dean welcomed her.

"How are you, Don" she nodded.

"Great as usual. Helen, you may not think singing is your forte, but girl, I like your vocals."

"Thanks Don, I think," Helen said, giving him an odd look.

"RCA Victor wants to broadcast our evening performances on the radio," Dean proclaimed proudly.

"A radio show, with me singing? On the level?" Then her face turned suspicious. "Are you pulling my leg, Don? That isn't very nice."

The musician laughed at her doubtful expression. "On the level, Helen, honest. Concluded a deal with the company this morning."

That evening Helen waited, seated center stage with the band, adorned in an elegant pale blue gown. She rose on cue, approaching the RCA microphone for her vocals,

So you met someone who set you back on your heels,
goody goody;
You met someone and now you know how it feels,
goody goody...

*

Drifting off to sleep in the wee hours of early morning, it came to her: *just imagine; my voice carried across the quiet of this mysterious country, singing into the dark Pampas and Patagonian night.* Pleased with the image, Helen yielded to fitful sleep.

*

Chum dialed through a trunk telephone call to the Club, just before a dinner show. Breathlessly reaching the telephone backstage, she heard, "You there, Helen!?"

"Yes, Chum, it's me" Helen answered forcefully. "You sound like you are calling from inside a tunnel."

"How did you guess?" he laughed. "Honey, I know you're getting ready to go on stage, but I needed to hear your voice. I miss you a lot. Is everything okay? Are you keeping safe?" His voice remained friendly, but she heard his intensity.

"Hunky dory, so far, except that I miss you badly," Helen admitted.

"I know. This is tough, but you stay strong, and we will be on our way to New York before you know it."

"I've got to go on, Chum. Promise to hold me in your dreams tonight, because I will dream of you."

"All right, sweetheart. Stay safe and I will see you soon."

"The time has come," Helen sighed, hanging up the phone. Turning the situation over in her mind while removing her silk robe, she decided, *Mother knows, but won't acknowledge Chum until I make it clear that we are a couple.*

After the final curtain, still resolved, Helen dug through her night table, where she found a piece of hotel stationary. Her left hand held down the thick paper while she carefully penciled a letter home. Beginning cautiously, the first bit of information she revealed was that her beau was a pilot.

Chum is a marvelous pilot, but don't worry; I've only gone flying with him once. And from my limited experience flying is perfectly safe and I honestly wanted to see Rio from the air. But now that I'm here in BA my chances of flying are nil anyway. Mother, Chum is so level-headed and ambitious. He's such a gentleman and his prospects look so bright. Graciously, he even took me to his tailor and bought me a handmade suit! I just know you will approve of both Chum and the suit, hee hee.

Love,

Helen

Focusing her letter on Chum left her more anxious than relieved. How her mother answered mattered more than anything to the smitten girl. Helen had clearly revealed her heart, and now had to wait for her mother's crucial blessing. Generally Bertha had disregarded earlier references to any young man, except Grant Garrett. However, after reading Helen's adulations, the girl hoped Bertha could see this relationship was much, much more.

"I'll guard it, with my life, Helen," Paul Youngs teased, patting the envelope in his top uniform pocket. As promised, both of Chum's friends had dropped by the club every few days from Rio to check on her. Yet, even with her faster air mail service, the time still passed too slowly for the apprehensive girl.

Finally, six days later, the crucial reply was slipped into her mail slot at the hotel. Helen, suffering a spasm of nerves, carefully slit open the envelope. Puffing out tension she read her mother's reaction. Bertha began slowly, covering general chitchat first. She filled her daughter in on Eileen, Mrs. Whalen, her arthritis, and things of that nature.

Appearing down a few paragraphs, the letter from New York finally acknowledged her daughter's news. "About your young man, it sounds like you're in love." Again, Helen repeated the words aloud. "It sounds like you're in love." Wasn't much, but it was enough to free Helen's heart. The girl directly seized more stationary and answered, "It's true, and not puppy love either." *Now* Mother understood. In the same envelope, Bertha forwarded an additional note she had received from Elie. Not happy to see this folded insert, Helen, of course, couldn't help but read it. Postmarked from Toronto it read:

> *My Dear Mrs. Thompson*
> *I am on the trip I had previously described and not received any word from Helen.*

Bertha had underlined the next lines:

> *I am wondering why I have not heard from Helen to whom I have written several letters and postcards, both to Brazil and New York. I am on my way to Japan if war rumors subside & would appreciate hearing from you as to Helen's whereabouts.*

Lighting a cigarette, the girl sat on the edge of the hotel bed, reminiscing about this kind young Belgian, who had loved and pursued her ardently, who happily waited for her outside stage doors, regardless of the hour or the weather— pursued her across most of Europe and the span of the Atlantic, and who now, ultimately, lost her to a boy from Virginia. She would have to tell Elie about her commitment to Chum, despite how awkward and painful. "I owe Elie that much," she whispered, crushing out her cigarette in the dark hotel room.

*

By the second week of her engagement, as Helen performed on the radio every night, the show grew to be quite popular with Argentine listeners. Mr. Koserin recognized her success on the RCA show when he cabled her from Rio,

> *Don Dean desires to offer you a full year contract.*

Congratulations on your well-deserved success in Buenos Aires, Helen!

Koserin

Mr. Koserin's good news and warm wishes floored her. The telegram lay face up on her hotel bed, while Helen stooped over, rereading his unexpected message.

I'm 24 years old, and have devoted my life to experience a moment like this. Now what do I do? This contract could mean stardom in Argentina, she silently considered. *And I don't want it. Not now. Not without Chum in my life. A year at Don Dean's? I'm hardly able to push through these two weeks.*

That's when she panicked. It dawned on Helen that she could be forced to stay. Pulling her contract out from her trunk, the girl began combing through the fine print. It could possibly be that Mr. Koserin had legal grounds to hold her to the Buenos Aires extension. If the club insisted on exercising their option she quite possibly wouldn't be allowed to leave.

Adding to her woes, a floor manager had recently been shadowing the dancer at her every turn. She had made it clear his attention was unwelcome, but her words made no difference. He waited at the entrance each afternoon, brought her flowers, hovered around her dressing room door, and basically watched her the rest of the time. Helen knew she had to reach out to Chum.

She sent off an urgent cable to Rio before rehearsal the following day.

Chum. Trouble with my contract, club may force option. Floor manager doesn't understand no. I need you.

Love,
Helen

322

*

"Damnation, Helen," he scowled. "I knew something like this would happen! I warned you," he shouted down the apartment hallway. The pilot marched directly to his bedroom, dragging an overnight bag from the closet.

"There a fire somewhere, Chum?" Paul had poked his head in, drawn by the commotion.

Chum barked at his roommate. "Helen needs my help."

"In Buenos Aires? Chum, don't you have that appointment at the ministry?"

"I have to go and settle things. There's been some trouble."

Inside the pilot's thoughts stormed, *rushing down to Argentina seemed like the last thing I planned today. I hope her contract has some loopholes. And that club floor manager! Damn it, I knew she'd have trouble like that.*

Chum paused, standing up, surprised by his own reaction. *Helen has altered my life, no question about that. I don't want her so far away. Knew she shouldn't go to Argentina, damn, but I can take care of that and get her the hell out of there.*

"Hey, hey, slow down buddy," Paul replied, concerned.

"She's in a jam, Paul. I need to get going. The Club is trying to hold her over and we need to get to New York. We've made our plans!"

"Look, Chum, you're upset. Please think about taking a commercial flight. I've got passes and Steve takes off to BA in a couple hours. At least do that."

Chum stood silently by his closet, considering his friend's advice. Holding his bag in one hand and a clean shirt in the other, he turned around, calmer, and said, "You're probably right."

Paul smiled and patted his friend on the shoulder. "Let me lend a hand."

Boarding an airboat in the harbor terminal, Chum passed Steve on the flight deck, his friend plainly confused.

He'll be back here soon enough to get the lowdown, Chum figured. Seated for the evening flight, it occurred to him he hadn't stopped moving since opening Helen's telegram. Resting his head back on the seat, the young man began to take stock of his and Helen's situations. He worked out a number of scenarios, finally making his decision. Landing after midnight, the young pilot exchanged a few brief words with Bancroft, then exited the clipper, hailed a taxi, and headed straight to Helen's hotel.

She had been crying. Coming through the door, Chum pulled her close.

"This will work out fine. I think I have a solution to all this mess. Helen, you know this situation is nuts," he complained, gesturing around the hotel room. He next looked fiercely into those sparkling eyes. "I can't accomplish one damn thing at work without thinking of you. I can't eat a meal without wondering if you would like the food. I think about what you're doing, how you're feeling every moment you are out of my sight."

Helen retreated to a chair and sat very still, certain she shouldn't have imposed on him. He clearly wasn't thrilled about the interruption to his schedule to help her out of her contract. New tears leaked down her cheeks.

Taking in Helen's pain, his expression quickly shifted, mirroring her vulnerability.

"Other people get married when they feel so, so ah—damn it, I can't even explain how the hell I feel!"

He stopped and looked intently at the girl. Then he again spoke, in a softer tone. "I can't have you so far away, Helen. We should probably get married just to find some peace." She bolted from her chair in a blur.

"I don't want to live without you, either," she whispered as she laid her head on his chest.

"You quit this show, and I'll clear my desk. I'll follow you as soon as possible to New York.

"But my contract...." Helen's voice trembled.

"Let's have a look, honey," Chum answered.

He sat at a little table, carefully reading through the agreement, occasionally asking questions. "Do you have your train ticket to

Rio?"

"I do. And my Munson ticket to New York, too," she assured him.

He exhaled, looking relieved and announced, "Koserin can't do anything if you break your contract. If he held your tickets, well, that would be another thing altogether. You are...*we* are free and clear to leave, once you finish the rest of this week. Now Helen, it's late, love, and we can't do anything else tonight. Let's get some sleep. We'll take care of the rest in the morning."

Helen's eyes were still red and puffy, but a peaceful smile replaced her dread. He led his girl to the little bed where they found solace and peaceful intimacy.

*

Hand in hand, Helen guided Chum to the club·near eleven in the morning.

"It's him; he's the one," she whispered quietly, pointing out the offending floor manager, who was absently polishing cocktail glasses. His face harsh, Chum approached the offender, tapped him on the shoulder, and glared at the man. The manager blanched, glancing at Helen, understanding without an interpreter.

"As far as she is concerned," Chum cocked his head toward a nervous, but glowering Helen, "you keep away. If I hear a word... "

"No, no, no problems, she belongs with you, I did not know," stammered the intimidated manager. Chum's approach did the trick; the manager ignored the girl the rest of her stay.

Later that morning, Chum typed a strong letter to Koserin that insisted on Helen's free agency regarding her contract.

Writing as the dancer, Chum stated,

> *After my final performance with Don Dean I am returning to Rio. From there I am departing to the United States. I choose not to accept the extension, and from my understanding of the contract you cannot hold me.*

*

Her co-workers at the club were pleased with Helen and Chum's engagement. Don Dean, himself, hosted and toasted the young couple at his home for a glittering celebration dinner. They both reveled in the warm first recognition of their commitment, finally publicly declaring their love. All the two did that evening was smile endlessly, and bask in hugs and good wishes. That night, Helen and Chum were simply happy.

But, all too soon the party ended, and the following morning Chum had to fly back to Rio de Janeiro to finish up his business obligations.

Later that same morning a telegram arrived at the club, addressed to her. Opening the small envelope Helen read,

> *You did not need to use such impertinent language with me.*
> *I was not going to interfere with your return. The suggestion*
> *was offensive to me, and an insult to my reputation.*
>
> *Koserin*

She felt a bit contrite for overreacting, but still rejoiced in her liberation. She was free to go home and plan her wedding.

Once the final broadcast was over and her trunk packed, Helen boarded the train for Brazil. From her berth, watching hours of scenery pass, the girl reflected on her situation. She and Eileen had always been Bertha's only financial support. What, if anything, would marriage do to change that obligation? She was troubled, but also trusted that Chum would understand and help her.

On the other side, Helen had to tell Bertha of her engagement before anything else, and her mother's likely response worried her. Marriage was a big leap from Helen's earlier puppy love comment.

Unable to unravel these problems at the moment, Helen decided to savor her last days with Chum until a ship carried her home to New York. She comforted herself that, with Chum's help, her difficulties would work themselves out.

*

Driving to the airfield back in Rio, Chum was pleased with the outcome of his trip to Buenos Aires. He was certain that, after all the Don Dean trouble, Helen would never want to step on another stage. His protective impulses guiding his thoughts, he knew she never needed to work again. He would take care of her.

CRYING BUCKETS

Bertha
New York
1936

Once he proposed, Chum became single-minded in his efforts to make their marriage happy. Before Helen's train arrived, returning from Buenos Aires, he had a long talk with his friends about getting married.

"You want this to work out with Helen, right?" Paul asked.

"I do," the future groom swiftly responded. For a moment three blank faces paused, then laughed lightly at his inadvertent pun. As the humor faded, Steve grew serious.

"Then you're going to have to quit Waco," Bancroft flatly announced.

"Why? We managed all right in between my flights and meetings," Chum replied a bit shocked. In fact, his sales region had grown exponentially by late summer –he now represented the company throughout the whole of South America. For Waco, his was a tremendous achievement. No other sales representative had found such success abroad. Hugh Perry and the rest of the firm lavished praises on Chum every time he opened his mail.

"Be realistic, buddy. With your job, you never know when or where you'll be called to the field," Paul Youngs pointed out.

"That is true," he responded uncertainly. Chum understood only too well what his friends were trying to tell him, he had already thought about how much his job took him away from her.

"We've watched you drop plans at a moment's notice," added Steve, "to fly some toy soldier or another to the interior— demonstrate a piece of aircraft, or rush to a meeting downtown."

"So, Chum, we've decided that you should apply with Pan American."

The pilot's chin jerked up in surprise. Paul continued.

"Relatively speaking, airline captains have a more settled life. Sure, we're gone a lot but all that is scheduled in advance."

"We can make commitments ahead of time, and keep them," Steve added, persuasively.

Chum sat quietly, mulling over their words, and he knew his friends were right. Both Paul and Steve flew limited hours a month, and the rest of their time belonged to them.

"Plus, and this is a big plus, Chum, we both actually like our jobs," Paul emphasized. The company takes good care of us, and the routes are, well, they are incredible. Recife, Belem, Paramaribo, Havana, Miami, all gorgeous. Plus, the stopovers in New York make home feel a lot closer. Helen could visit her mother when she wanted. You two could live here, in paradise, enjoy your life together, the money is pretty fair, and it goes a lot further than in the States."

Considering their advice as he motored to the train station, Chum decided his friends knew what they were talking about. The Waco job had always meant making himself available to his clients at their leisure, not his. Helen deserved a husband at home, someone she could count on.

By the time he stepped on the rail platform, Chum had made up his mind. He kissed his girl hello as she joyfully hopped off the train, announcing, "I'm quitting Waco, Helen."

Surprise and confusion colored her expression— she knew he loved his job. He explained the rest. "I've decided to take a job with Pan American, and we will still live here, in Rio, at the scene of the crime," he gathered her in an embrace, utterly happy.

*

She was lying on her side, fully awake, though it was well after 1:00 AM. Chum had fallen asleep curled around her, but she had since rolled him over. "I'll need earplugs to make this marriage work," she quietly said, listening to his unyielding, thunderous snoring. Gazing into the darkness, she turned to weightier matters—sharing her far-reaching news with her mother in New York.

Thinking aloud, Helen whispered to herself, "I have no other alternative. What I used to do before him hardly matters now. But how do I explain that to mother? She'll see this as a betrayal. She hasn't been here to see how my life has changed. And her days in New York haven't varied one iota. I wonder how many hours she's burned up on the telephone, complaining to Mrs. Whalen or Mr. Evans about my absence."

She winced at her next thought. *While mother is up there thumbing through trade papers for auditions, I'm down here planning my wedding. How do I tell her how differently I feel this time, how essential Chum has become in my life? And after what she did to Grant...!"*

Helen shuddered, picturing that banishment repeating with Chum.

Too distressed to sleep, Helen crept out of bed, reaching for her robe. She tiptoed to the kitchen, her eyes diverted by the twinkling lights of Rio lying beyond the glass balcony door. There she stood sipping a cup of water, gazing at the stunning nightscape, while her mind lingered on her intractable problem. Chum's indifferent snoring persisted, muffled by the apartment walls.

She couldn't delay any longer. Each day in Rio disappeared as quickly as steaming puddles after a jungle rain, and Helen's departure for New York drew closer. So it was with deep apprehension, while Chum was out flying, that she sat and carefully penned one of her most important letters home.

> *Dearest Mother,*
>
> *Though Don Dean is a very nice man and his wife is lovely too, one manager wasn't so friendly. Or should I say too friendly? The man followed me everywhere, even to my hotel. He sent me flowers all the time and barged into my dressing room without knocking. Oh, Bert, I've been so upset. And Mr. Koserin has made arrangements that I stay on in Buenos Aires for a YEAR. I worried that I had no choice, and then*

I cabled Chum to help me. He flew right down, sorted out the trouble, and fixed it so I can come home. Isn't he swell?

I've never met such a wonderful man; he's befriended me in so many ways. When Chum flew down to Buenos Aires to help me, we both decided we're in love with each other and want to get married. But, don't worry Bert. We aren't certain yet how the timing will go for the wedding, but I'm coming home to New York first. I'll be sailing north on the SS American Legion arriving by the end of August. Chum will follow me to New York as quickly as he can.

He has a lot of pending work still in Rio. We hope to tie the knot by early September, sometime around my birthday. Mother, you should know that Chum is the kindest and best person in the world, and he can even cook, so we won't starve!

The girl closed her note with the most difficult news—a part Helen knew could potentially spoil everything.

Bert, we plan to make Rio our home. Chum has taken a job with Pan American Airlines and will be based out of Brazil like his friends. Won't it be grand, you can come down any time to see us in beautiful Brazil? You'll never have to bear another New York winter again!

Once posted, the letter marked the beginning of a most difficult, extended waiting period. Helen obsessively checked the mail each morning.

At long last the moment came when Bertha's awaited response appeared in the mailbox. Nervously slicing the envelope open, Helen couldn't seem to keep her hands from trembling. She eased down at the kitchen table to wade through her mother's long epistle—and found she needed to reread the letter three or four times, struggling to unlock hidden meanings. Doubt began to settle in somewhere between her heart and stomach. Helen knew Bertha's familiar looped, upright cursive as distinctly as she knew her mother's face or voice.

Helen,

I am happy and sad, if you can figure that out. I'm glad you have decided to marry at home. But, I'm so sad you're leaving a promising, certain-to-be successful career in show business. I have always had great hopes of your getting someplace in your profession.

I've cried buckets since receiving your letter, and your big sister has shed a few too... your being so far away will be the hardest thing. You've been staying with him until the next ship sets out for New York. You could have left today as I sit down to write this letter, and you didn't. I am so hurt. At least you could have considered spending more time with your family in New York before going away for good.

Our time with you is limited and he will have you the rest of his life. I will be glad indeed to meet Chum, he must be special and I will let the rest of the family know of the impending nuptials.

The girl exhaled at Bertha's acquiescence. However, she could see her mother wasn't finished divulging her raw feelings.

All the while I've been writing, Eileen and her best friend, Billie, were rolling with laughter at me because I want to take Eileen somewhere to meet some nice fellow so she can get married too.

Well, it looks as though my dream of you being a star is over (and it makes me very sad). But we look forward to your return, and to give my best wishes to Chum.

Mother

Helen put her letter down, sitting back, her jaw tightening while pain seized her throat, and she worked hard to keep from crying. In anguish Helen asked herself, *am I being selfish? Doesn't she see that I can love them both? I can't bear to be away from Chum, and she will always be my dear mother.*

The boys weren't home, and Helen, too caught up in her thoughts, knew she needed to get out of the apartment. A walk on the beach sounded like the antidote she needed.

A full beach greeted the troubled girl, and the evident fun taking place around her seemed to help. Helen kicked off her shoes, feeling the warmth of sand beneath her feet. Using her hand to shade her eyes, Helen looked out toward the bay at the multitude of boats winding around the sparkling inlet.

Maybe I'm asking too much of Mother right now, she pondered. *I guess I can see how she might think I've abandoned her. All her efforts and hopes had been pinned on me to be a star. I'll try to be more patient with her, now that I have, in effect, brought an end to mother's dream.*

Helen walked back from the beach with a decidedly lighter step.

*

The bride-to-be found her good spirits short-lived. A day later, another letter arrived from New York, and clearly Bertha had second thoughts.

> *Helen,*
>
> *We are more than surprised and more than hurt that you did not come home on the boat from Buenos Aires, especially since Chum was down there with you for nearly two weeks. I figured you would have been working at the club until the boat sailed. We are glad you are going to get married if it means happiness to you, but it has given us heartaches we've never felt, that you did not come home to be with us as long as possible. You have given me more heartache, that after an absence of five months, you have continued to stay away. You left the Don Dean Club in Buenos Aires with plenty of time to catch an*

*earlier ship home. On one hand you regaled your success with
radio broadcasting out of the club, and then next thing, you
drop that you are engaged to be married.*

*The Munson schedules are limited and you won't be home
for your own birthday. Eileen will probably be gone on the
road with a new show. How could you be so thoughtless not to
consider these things?*

*Eileen is such a grand girl and thinks so much of you,
how could you not get home on the earlier ship and stay as long
as possible?*

Gloom and guilt reignited in her vulnerable heart. It was
becoming harder to keep her earlier resolve to be understanding
when Bertha showed such little forbearance.

MOTHERS

Rio de Janeiro
1936

"Why so low, darling? Did I do something wrong?"

"Oh, Chum, of course not. It's my mother and home that I'm worried about."

"I don't understand, what could be so wrong? Is your mother sick?"

"No, no, it's nothing like that. You see," she paused, "my mother and I are very, very close. Eileen, too" Helen began.

"I understand she has struggled, Helen. I'm quite close to my mother, too. I wish I could see her more than I do."

Helen exhaled, knowing her situation wasn't easy to explain, but she soldiered on. "She has lost a lot of people in her life, and has sacrificed so much for my career."

"I know. Mine's done a lot for me as well. She's a wonderful woman. Makes me feel guilty being so far away," Chum shared, trying to understand his girl.

"I've always lived with my mother and times were often tough," Helen faltered.

"And what, Helen?" She looked at him with love, his forehead was crinkled, his eyebrows raised, and she surrendered smiling,

"And nothing. My mother will love you, Chum. Not as much as I do, though," the girl carefully attempted a confident smile.

Her mother's rebuke had left the bride-to-be heavy with guilt, and worse, feeling like a deserter. Helen even began to question her right to marry, when she had such ongoing responsibilities to her mother.

Maybe mother is right, she worried.

Yet, she deeply loved her Chum. She loved his drawl, his

smile, his sense of decency—she loved him. The idea of letting him go—living without him, cancelling their wedding was beyond comprehension.

"Mother was right." Helen said aloud. "I should have returned to New York earlier and not lingered here with Chum. She would have taken my news better." So Helen packed for the next Rio departure, and understood when the S.S. *American Legion* reached Brooklyn at the end of August, her mother's outrage and recriminations would be there to greet her, as well.

*

The time after he kissed his girl goodbye at the docks did not pass easily. Helen was never far from his longing thoughts, and he sent one lonely letter after another to the Whitby Hotel in New York. Chum had to stay behind to wind up his final business obligations. He planned to sail north himself as soon as possible, and finally set a date for their wedding and honeymoon. But one incessant delay, followed by the next, made it impossible to book his own passage north. He vented his frustration, knowing she shared his anticipation.

> *Dearest Helen,*
>
> *I'm waiting endlessly for the Brazilian brass to make up their minds. They keep telling me tomorrow, then tomorrow comes and they put me off again. The officers argue over which planes and how many models they want to order. I traveled to the field and completed all the paperwork for the government's eventual aircraft order. As soon as the officers finally make their decision I will fill in the model numbers and lock the door and be on my way.*

Along with the vacillating Brazilian bureaucrats, Chum was also waiting for word from Pan American Airlines' office in New York. Exasperated by all these holdups, he admitted to Helen, "All this foot dragging is keeping me from you, and that makes me so damn mad."

*

Living with Bertha became a pressing ordeal for Helen from the moment she stepped on dry land. Scrutinizing the crowds from the deck of the *Legion*, the girl had easily distinguished tall, blonde Eileen, and tracing down her sister's arm near the elbow stood their little mousy-haired mother.

"Thank goodness Eileen came," Helen murmured, comforting herself. Carrying her purse and one small valise, the daughter grasped that she had missed her mother more than she realized, and rushed down the passageway.

"Didn't think you'd actually come home," Bertha snapped. "You look drawn."

The taxi ride home, uncomfortably silent, prompted nervous Helen to make small talk.

"Did Mother tell you, Eileen, that I did some singing on the radio?"

"That's what she told me, kid. Good for you. Maybe something like that will break here..." Eileen paused awkwardly; she knew Helen intended to leave show business altogether. Helen saw tears collecting in her mother's eyes, and rigid silence attended the rest of the ride home. The real clash waited until the apartment.

"This time it's real, mother," Helen gently asserted.

"Then what exactly have the last 24 years of your life been? A mirage?"

"If you would only wait to get to know Chum..."

Eileen quietly spoke, "Mother, calm down." Bertha fiercely turned, pointing her finger violently at her older daughter to butt out. Eileen shook her head and stepped in between her sister and her mother.

Bertha continued to assail her younger daughter. "I thought, Helen, that I knew you! All my support, all my plans for your success, all my sacrifices for your career, and your father's too, before he died. What would your father say of your breaking faith? All of your work and training! And now I am supposed to forget that, and give you up to some *stranger*?"

Helen dissolved into tears—a mix of guilt, shame, and anguish for her future hopes. But Bertha glared, unmoved.

"You believed Grant Garrett was the one, and look what a wastrel he was. And Elie, Helen, what about Elie? This boy, who has chased you around the world, gets nothing? How can you live with yourself?"

A pronounced silence settled as Bertha, out of words, simply shook, her hands white and trembling.

In the days following this anguishing attack, strain and exaggerated civility cast a chill over the apartment. Conversations were awkwardly forced and absent of any talk of Chum or of marriage. Helen's only relief from the stalemate came when his loving letters arrived from South America. Chum's naïve, sweet eagerness lifted her spirits, taking her back to the uncomplicated world of just the two of them.

And he didn't disappoint. In a letter to the Whitby, Chum raised the subject of their honeymoon, and suggested that they fly together to Miami.

> *Steve has vacation coming and plans to spend two weeks in Florida, fishing. If you're game we could rent a boat together and go deep-sea fishing with him, maybe out as far as Bimini in the Bahamas. You know we have lots of friends in Miami, there's swimming and also…an air show.*

The perennial silence in the apartment shattered. She threw her head back and really laughed for the first time since her return.

Oh, that feels better. Normal, happy. Fun sure has been missing from my life since I've come back. A honeymoon for three, now that is a novel idea—only Chum would think of that.

"I sure miss my guy," she lovingly whispered to no one. And

Helen again felt the warm current of happiness course through her. *As long as we are together, three is fine for our honeymoon—fishing, air show, and whatever else Chum cooks up.*

*

Helen's sudden laughter drew her mother out of the bedroom. Catching her daughter leaning over a letter, glowing, love clearly etched on her face prompted the mother to take a step back.

"Oh Mother, please don't cry." Helen scurried over to hug Bertha. "This is a happy time, a time of new beginnings!"

"No. This is the end." Bertha morosely stated, drawing in a shaky breath. "The end of hope, of stardom, of a bright future, of my family, of my life."

"But, Mother..." Helen began.

"No, Helen," Bertha interrupted. "You have no business getting married. Your abilities are limited to dancing and some singing. Not marriage. I have been married, and the commitment is not for a girl like you. You are foolish to believe you could make a marriage work. You need the guidance I provide, not this stranger you blindly and foolishly wish to impose upon our family. I have done nothing but sacrifice for your career, and getting married without my blessing is a poor way to repay my devotion."

"You don't understand how it feels when I'm with Chum." the girl protested.

"If you marry him and move to Brazil, to me you will be dead—as dead as my dear mother and my loving Floyd. You'll be just another person who abandoned me and left me alone. You'll be nothing more than a sorrowful, disappointing memory."

Horrific silence loomed, and tension filled the room. Helen could not catch her breath. Her mother stared straight ahead, her hands fisted tight, thin lips drawn, colorless with the strain.

Eileen had softly entered the room in time to hear Bertha's dramatic ultimatum. Bertha and Helen twisted their heads simultaneously, as Eileen lit a cigarette and glared at her mother.

The intensity in the room ratcheted.

"Mother, that's enough," she announced. "You cannot dictate to Helen how to live her life. I won't let her sacrifice her future for your convenience or gratification. People get married; that is normal. Helen is perfectly justified to marry the man she loves."

Bertha launched into her older daughter, shouting, "You stay out of this! This doesn't concern you!"

Eileen, unperturbed by the outburst, responded, "If you insist on pushing Helen around, you will ruin her happiness and her life. Is that what you mean to do to her? To ruin her life with your own selfishness?"

Helen quietly whispered, "Thank you, Eileen."

"Of course, little sister. Now, Bertha, there will be no more talk of meddling with Helen's wedding. You will behave properly and support her plans. You will behave cordially with Chum. He must never know how awful you've been about the wedding. Do you hear me? Do you understand me, Mother?"

Bertha answered her adamant, older daughter with a defiant glare.

*

"So, young Montgomery, I understand you are soon to leave us. Have Joaquin and I been so fickle about ordering aircraft that you must resign your job?"

"No, Colonel. My time here has been pure pleasure. I am getting married soon in New York, then returning to Rio de Janeiro to take you to lunch every week."

"Ha. I look forward to your return, Montgomery. I shall be glad to dine in your company whenever you wish. Excuse my rude presumptions, but have you made wedding arrangements, yet? Perhaps purchased the wedding bands or engagement ring? If not, I can recommend a jeweler, a fine man who will negotiate with you a fair price. He is my brother-in- law," the Brazilian colonel grinned broadly.

Chum, with an astonished expression, replied, "Sir, I would be very grateful for the referral. I've never shopped for anything like wedding rings before. Thank you, sir."

It was true. The lovesick boy hadn't thought of, nor had any idea of how to begin this vital assignment. Deciphering the makeshift diagram his military friend drew, Chum finally located a little shop at the base of the foothills. Opening a thick glass door, noting the iron gates retracted aside the shop's façade, the American met a kind-faced Brazilian. The owner stood smiling behind a long, cloudy, glass jewelry case. The white tile floor appeared dingy, but tidy. Hanging light fixtures, designed to feature the sparkling contents in the cases, merely reflected scratches and a misty sheen.

Addressing Chum in Portuguese, the merchant inquired, "Que eu seja de serviço?" Chum, nothing close to fluent in the language, stumbled through a few phrases trying to convey his errand.

The shopkeeper nodded, gathering the pilot's task, and raised velvet and satin boxes one after another onto the opaque counter. Happily, the jeweler described in Portuguese and using gestures, each piece, pointing out such things as carat size and the clarity of the gems. Chum soon selected his choice using his own hand signals. The helpful merchant, obviously tipped off by his wife's brother, attempted some English of his own, pronouncing slowly, "What size, please?" Chum gawked blank-faced at the shop owner.

"Size? I'm not sure, maybe about five foot four, one hundred ten pounds," he estimated, bewildered.

Now, the jeweler's expression altered, clearly puzzled. "No, no, not—this," he clarified, pointing to the aquamarine.

"Rings have sizes? He realized he didn't understand the first thing about rings. Chum had a letter to write to New York.

> *Darling,*
> *I went ring shopping for our wedding; figure I can get a better deal here for jewelry than in New York. Would you please go to a dime store and buy a ring that fits you? I can take it in to the jewelers here and buy yours in the right size.*

Wait, on second thought a toy ring might not work, too lumpy to seal in an envelope. Instead make a paper ring that you can flatten in a letter. Cut a strip of paper wrap it around your finger and airmail it to Rio. Not your finger, just the paper. You won't be disappointed with the outcome, I promise.
Until we are together again,
Love, Chum

*

"I'll get it," Eileen called, dashing to the apartment door. Helen's older sister came face to face with a tall, friendly-faced man in a blue uniform who bore gold wings on his lapel, and on a billed cap. He looked back at her, his face first reflecting familiar friendship before it clouded in confusion. Suddenly a motion at Eileen's side distracted her, as Helen flew under Eileen's right elbow and into Steve Bancroft's arms.

"Steve!" the girl sang. "By any chance did you bring Chum in your suitcase?"

He laughed, "For a second I thought you'd answered the door, but I see it's your taller twin."

"Steve, Eileen. Eileen, Steve. That clear things up?" Helen laughed. Both her sister and friend smiled, amused by her enthusiasm.

"Got something here for you, Helen. Chum trusted me with some hot cargo," her welcome friend announced.

Bertha crept into the hall, standing on the far side of the door. Formally she chided, "Aren't you going to ask your guest inside, Helen?"

At the same time, Eileen and Helen chimed together, "Come in, Come in. Sorry, please have a seat, Gee, Steve, sorry."

"Steve, this is our mother, Bertha Thompson. Mother this is Steve Bancroft, a good friend of Chum's and mine." Helen beamed at her unexpected guest.

"Would you like a cup of coffee, Mr. Bancroft?" Bertha asked.

"It's Steve, Mrs. Thompson, and no thank you. I really can't stay long. As I said, I'm here on a special errand from one M.J. Chumbley."

At that pronouncement, Steve extracted a small, hinged satin box. Before the three astonished women, he opened the dark blue container, revealing a beautiful engagement ring.

"Let's see if I can repeat what he told me." Steve grinned, staring upward like a school boy, and recited, "Helen, this is a nine carat aquamarine with six diamonds surrounding it. I hope that the fit is right, and please don't kiss Steve. Remember, Helen, it's me you're marrying."

"Oh my goodness!" were the only words Helen could utter, as she fit the ring on her left hand. And despite Chum's forewarning, Helen hugged Steve, throwing her arms around his middle.

Eileen snatched Helen's hand at once, examining the exquisite, clear blue-green stone. Bertha, though gracious to Chum's friend, said nothing about his mission or the glittering ring. Remaining a little longer, Steve eventually excused himself (for a date, he whispered to Helen) then to the hotel for a good night sleep before his return flight south in the morning.

When the apartment door closed, Bertha, without a word to her girls, vanished to her room. Eileen, paying no attention to her mother's antics, kept up some good-natured ribbing with her sister. "Gee whiz, kid! How you able to lift that hand hauling that boulder around? Hey, Helen, can I take a dive in all that blue? Boy, this guy must like you a lot. Did you clobber him over the head, or slip something in his drink?"

And when she finished the teasing, Eileen settled for frequent, piercing "cat-call" whistles. Eileen could shatter glass with those, and still her mother's door remained sealed.

Bumping her sister with her shoulder and rolling her eyes at her mother's behavior, Helen quickly scribbled a joyous note to her betrothed:

You, (and Steve) truly surprised me and I love you and the ring very much. You are such a good picker.

A week later, Chum happily responded to his bride-to-be:

> *Sorry you can't say the same about being a good picker, because now you are getting stuck with me. Honey, the stone wasn't as big as others, but absolutely clear, best gem of its kind. I have purchased a platinum band too, but we will have it engraved when I get to New York, because we don't know the wedding date yet. Cabled my mother. She is thrilled. Wants us to visit as soon as we can.*
>
> *Your Chum*

*

All at once, events moved swiftly. Though October still found Chum trapped in Rio, and his nerves stretched to the breaking point, the air ministry miraculously decided to execute their aircraft order. He rushed to the airfield, as though his car had wings, and completed the paper work. Rifling through a lower desk drawer, the impatient groom seized the documents he needed. Slapping them on top of the desk, he noticed a telegram lying diagonally under the Waco order forms. Exhaling in a long sigh, his frenzy died away, and Chum leaned slowly back in his swivel chair.

After a moment, he reached for a letter opener and unfolded the cable, pushing the aircraft business aside.

> *Congratulations, Montgomery Chumbley. Pan American is pleased to announce your new position as a clipper co-pilot, based in Rio de Janeiro. Juan Trippe and the Board of Directors extend their welcome and look forward to meeting you in Miami at Dinner Key. Contact our office at your earliest convenience.*

"Boy, when it rains, it pours," he murmured in disbelief. He folded the telegram, tucking the note into his pocket. Returning his attention to pressing business, Chum cranked an order form into the roller of his typewriter. Taking care to avoid mistakes, he pecked the model numbers into the proper boxes. That done, the pilot hurried back to town, stopping at the Western Union office to catch Helen up on the rapid turn of events.

Helen—Finished airplane order. Pan Am cabled. They want me. Waiting on the Munson now. Things here buttoned up. Will arrive end of October. Hold On.

Your Chum

Back at the apartment, he happily elaborated on his news in a letter to his bride-to-be:

My business mailbox and cable reception are now officially closed. I will only accept yours and they can arrive anytime till I leave. My darling girl, I leave here on October 22 and arrive to New York November 5th. I'm hoping to be met by a ravishing blond, and her wonderful family of females. So, again, my special girl, you have a date to meet me at the docks in Brooklyn, and from then on?
Who loves you, and how much?

Chum

ACKNOWLEDGEMENTS

I did not set out to be a writer. As a child, if asked, I would have responded "I think I'd like to be a teacher, or do something with American History." I like history. A lot. So, to turn to writing came as much a surprise to me as anyone else. But, my friends and family have been steadfast in their support. When I needed a pat on the back or a willing ear, these people stepped up. For these good folks, I bear nothing but gratitude and affection.

Foremost, I wish to thank my mother, Rita Olson who patiently answered my many questions about arcane past details.

To sweet Alice Johnson, who sat me down and taught me to write—your gift I cannot repay.

I also wish to thank my first fan, Bev Jarvis, who graciously listened to my story, seeing the potential when I could not.

To Kim Foster and Yvonne Rousseau, both of whom took me seriously when I offered the manuscript for their perusal.

Lastly, I wish to thank the legions of students who passed through my classroom. You placed your trust in me, nurturing a self confidence that made challenging this book possible.

Gail
The Cabin in the Mountains
2014

ABOUT
THE AUTHOR

Gail Olson Chumbley is a public school retiree after 33 years in the classroom. A nationally recognized instructor of American History, Gail was ready make the transition from telling the tales of the past, to trying her hand at writing those stories for a broader audience.

A particular specialty in Gail's repertoire was sending legions of teenagers to record oral histories in the community. Students brought back extraordinary narratives of World War Two soldiers, memories of the Great Depression, and a few recordings of the endless walking at Woodstock in 1969. Gail's work has been honored with the Preserve America award in 2004 co-sponsored by the White House and Gilder Lehrman Institute. In 2005, Gail received the Outstanding Teacher of American History from National Daughters of the American Revolution in Washington DC. She appears in the Congressional Record of the 109th Congress, with remarks given by Senator Mike Crapo on May 12, 2005. The Senator highlighted her work in the Veterans Oral History Project in conjunction with the Library of Congress. In a two-year campaign Gail led her students in raising funds for the National World War Two Memorial topping all other schools in nation. She and student representatives personally delivered the funds to Senator Robert Dole in 2002.

Her usage of recorded recollections began with a grant from the Idaho Humanities Council sending her to Miami to interview her father-in-law, Montgomery "Chum" Chumbley. From that initial project, her first non-reference book evolved, *River of January*.

For the author, this labor of love grew into a single-minded resolve to recount the lives of two extraordinary people: Montgomery Chumbley, and Helen Thompson Chumbley. Gail met Chad Chumbley in 1994, after he happened to show up on her front porch. Chad brought with him the dramatic story of his aviation pioneer father, and glamorous showgirl mother. He had little understanding of the width and breadth of his parents' accomplishments, until he unearthed their massive accumulation of papers and records, while cleaning out his childhood home. Though nearly twenty years in the making, *River of January* grew from the union of the author and her husband. Gail toyed with prospect of committing Helen and Chum's story to paper, but procrastinated until moved to complete the project as a result of her husband's perilous bout with cancer.

A child of the Pacific Northwest, the author was born and raised in Spokane, Washington, receiving her history degree from Western Washington University in Bellingham. Gail is the mother of two grown children from a previous marriage. After her retirement in May of 2013, Gail and her husband settled in the Idaho Mountains above Boise. They have made their home in a little cabin in the woods where she has embarked on a writing career, while Chad attempts to play golf.

For more information on Gail Chumbley and River of January, go to www.river-of-january.com.

SONG CREDITS

Black Coffee – Paul Francis Webster and Sonny Burke, 1948

First You Have Me High – Harold Arlen, 1936

Goody Goody – Johnny Mercer and Matty Malneck, 1936

I've Got to Get Hot – Jack Yellen and Ray Henderson, 1935

What Would You Do? – Leo Robin and Richard A. Whiting, 1932

You're the Top – Cole Porter, 1934

PART TWO

River of January: Figure Eight

Seated in the little Whitby apartment, Chum opted for the couch next to Helen, readily grasping her hand, as Bertha along with Eileen settled in matching wingback chairs. The room grew awkwardly silent, apart from an idling toilet that finally rattled to a sudden halt. It was Bertha who broke the stillness.

"My daughter tells me you are taking her away to South America." Helen's eyes bulged in mortification.

Chum, misunderstanding her meaning, smiled easily, "Mrs. Thompson, I will take good care of her. You never need to worry about Helen," he began. "We would love to have you visit, and you too, Eileen. And of course with my flights to New York, she can come up and spend time with you here."

"I see," Bertha coldly retorted.

Helen, fully horrified, again attempted to redirect the conversation, alarmed by her mother's cold expression. "Eileen, have I told you what a skilled pilot Chum is?" She blurted impetuously. Eileen caught her sister's tone and played along, sensing mother's growing rage.

"You said he won an air race," The older sister encouraged.

Chum, affably spoke up, "It was called the Darkness Derby, and it ended here, right out at Roosevelt Field. I had a lot of fun."

Bertha's fingers began tapping the arm of her worn chair. She began beating them in sequence from her little finger to her file finger, where the drumming began again. Even Chum began to identify the growing tension.

Eileen hopped up, "Look at the time! We really must get going to dinner. What eatery have you missed the most while you've been gone, Chum? Blossoms? Mori's? Sazarac's?"

Smiling again, Chum replied, "I think maybe Mori's. Dinner is on me, ladies." .

"I'm afraid I cannot join you," Bertha flatly stated. Helen's face again reflected her edgy fears. "If I am to host a party, I need to begin preparations."

"Maybe we could order in, then, and help you?" Chum offered politely.

"No, no," the three women answered in a chorus. Then they began excuses at once,

"I have to make my list," Bertha declared with finality.

"Mother needs us out of her hair, so she can plan," Helen added, her voice a tad too shrill.

"We can help her best by getting out of here," Eileen chimed in.

Wearing a puzzled expression, Chum helped Helen on with her coat, politely turning toward Eileen, but she was by then adjusting her jacket on her shoulders.

Saying their goodbyes, the three ventured out under the Whitby awning, and the cutting air succeeded in restoring their earlier enthusiasm. "Where'd you say, Chum?" Helen smiled, feeling lighter again away from her mother.

"Well, Eileen mentioned Mori's, and my mouth got to watering for Italian. Are you ladies willing to travel down to the Village for a little spaghetti?"

"Lead on, my almost brother-in-law," Eileen kidded with a grin.

Seated around a small square table, draped in an immaculate, white table cloth, Chum leaned back as a waiter reached over to light the center candles. That done, the white tapers silently beginning to glow, he turned directly and addressed his bride-to-be. "Now, no fooling around with me, Helen, what's going on with your mother?"